MW00605662

Apartment Building Millionaire Workbook

Step-by-Step Guide to Finding & Buying Passive Income Real Estate

Written By:

Monica Main

Publisher: Global Success Strategies
Cover Design: Peter Fasolino and Rafael Po
Production and Composition: Cindy Thompson and Lea Loponen

This publication is designed to provide accurate and authoritative information in regard to the subject matter covered. It is sold with the understanding that the publisher and author are not engaged in rendering legal, accounting or other professional services. If legal advice or other expert assistance is required, the services of a competent professional should be sought.

Library of Congress Cataloging-in-Publication Data
      Main, Monica S., 1974—
      [Apartment building millionaire workbook]
      Apartment building millionaire workbook / by Monica Main
      p. cm.
ISBN-10: 0-9829294-2-0 (alk. paper)
ISBN-13: 978-0-9829294-2-1 (alk. paper)
   1. Real estate investment. 2. Real estate investment---Finance. 3. Cash flow. I. Title

GLOBAL SUCCESS

www.Global-Success-Strategies.com

How to Use This Workbook

This workbook is the companion to *Apartment Building Millionaire*. It's essential that you have *Apartment Building Millionaire* in order to effectively work through the exercises presented in this workbook.

Please read *Apartment Building Millionaire* from cover to cover first before attempting to complete the exercises and assignments as outlined in this step-by-step workbook. It will give you a better understanding of how apartment building investing works, my methodology of investing, and basic terminology needed to understand some of the investment strategies I cover in these exercises.

Some tools you will need as a serious real estate investor are as follows:

1) A recent copy of your personal credit report from all 3 credit bureaus (Experian, Equifax, and TransUnion).

2) A *Premium LoopNet Membership* through **www.LoopNet.com**.

3) A log of your progress including agents you've spoken to, letter campaigns you've done, serious property deals you are working on, etc. You may want to get a 3-ring notebook with tabs to help keep you organized. You may want to get a set of those cheap tabs that consist of 5 or 8 tabs to keep yourself better organized. Your tabs may look something like this:
    a. Research
    b. Follow-Up Log (with Agents)
    c. Letter Campaign Log
    d. Property Deal Log
    e. Serious Property Deals

4) A handheld calculator.

5) A computer with Internet access.

6) A *supportive* spouse; other family members should not be notified of your activities as a real estate investor or you'll have to deal with the negative "nay-sayer" syndrome. If you have a spouse who is not on board, quickly get your life partner on your team by doing a *presentation of a lifetime* showing the lifelong cash flow benefits of long-term residential-commercial real estate investments. Dealing with a negative spouse will greatly hinder your ability in being successful in this business.

7) If you want to do letter campaigns, consider where you will be getting mailing list leads. Although this company is pricey, I recommend using **www.ProspectNow.com**. If you call them and mention promotional code "MM" or "Monica Main" then you will get a discount. Only sign up if you are *very serious* about wanting to do letter campaigns.

Part I:
GETTING STARTED

Exercise #1
Recognizing Defeat

Every single self-made millionaire and billionaire has suffered some kind of major defeat or setback that could have been the end of their attempts at becoming successful in business. This could have been a bankruptcy, legal loss, business loss, or any other financial loss that resulted in losing everything.

As with the loss of someone close to you, losing out financially in a big way also requires grieving. Not everyone is ready to jump back into life when losing a close loved one. Not everyone will be able to jump back into life after suffering a major setback such as a bankruptcy. Working through the "grieving" process is required if you are to re-establish yourself.

Once you "snap" back into the real world after appropriately grieving your financial loss, you can then push yourself back into action and towards success. Financial loss should not be a reason to permanently put you "out of business," so to speak.

If you have experienced a major setback or financial loss, you are in good company. Every other self-made millionaire out there also has experienced at least one bankruptcy. Many of them suffered several major financial losses.

If you have suffered from some financial devastations and losses, I can tell you that having these major setbacks will only allow you to see that, after everything is said and done, you are actually okay in the end. Once you realize that the setback knocked you down but you are still alive and well, you can then say, "Hey, I lost everything and I'm okay! It's not nearly as bad as I thought it would be. I'm not dead. I'm not broken. Here I am. I'm breathing. I have a roof over my head. I have food on the table. I'm actually okay!"

Please take the time to ask yourself these questions:

1) Have you ever had any major financial setbacks such as a bankruptcy or legal issue that completely wiped you out and/or changed your life? Please explain these challenges.

2) If you had experienced at least one major financial setback, have you gone through the "grieving" process yet? Have you gotten over the loss or are you still grieving the loss? Are you ready to "snap" back into action or do you still need some time to grieve?

3) If you are not ready to push forward again toward success, what is stopping you? Are you lacking in motivation and drive? Are you waiting for the right opportunity to excite you? Are you afraid to move forward because you believe that "they" will take it all away from you again?

Exercise #2
Understanding the Economic Changes

Globally our entire world is changing. It would have been laughable in the 1950s to consider that China would be our new world power. Now, as of this writing, China is now the 2nd largest economy in the world, beating out Japan by a slim margin who now settles in 3rd place. It's been predicted for the past couple of decades that China would be Number One. They are saying that it will more than likely happen in the next 20 years. I predict that it will happen in the next 10 years or less.

Is this something to freak out about? Not really. Most people don't know that many of the Asian countries have had real estate and business interests in the United States for several decades already. The U.S. has been borrowing money from China and Japan with great fervor for quite some time. We are essentially in debt to them. You can never be in a position of power when you owe someone something. Since this is the case, I believe we lost our power a long time ago.

Instead of being fearful as most Americans are, you need to learn how to analyze what is going on so that you can be ahead of the game. Don't be fearful, don't exude hatred, and don't panic! Look, study, watch, and listen…then *act* when the right time comes.

It's easy to get sucked into negative media by watching nail-biting news reports about how Social Security is evaporating, unemployment rates are rapidly increasing, and we're going into Round 2 of our "double-dip" recession…or depression, whichever way you look at it.

But I see things differently. You see, when the 1930s Great Depression hit, people were standing in soup lines that extended down city blocks. People showed up in large riot-like packs to possibly catch a lucky break to be an overworked, underpaid day laborer at the docks. My husband's grandfather jumped on trains and stole coal to heat his family's abode for one more day while taking weekend gigs as a bare-knuckled street fighter to get paid chump while his bookies made money on illegal bets.

In today's "depression" you don't see such things. Nobody has a job or money, according to the media, yet I'll go to my local *Red Lobster* on a lazy Tuesday evening and the place is packed with a waiting list. People are so "broke" that they are running to this pricey seafood restaurant to pop a minimum of $85 on a "cheap" meal because they are so broke and unemployed. *Apple* had just recently released a new product: the *iPad*. People waited in long lines starting from the night before and camped out on a sidewalk just to be the first to buy this overpriced gadget with barely enough utilities to make it worth the purchase. Apparently things are so "bad" that nobody is working or has any money but yet people are still eating out, buying senseless overpriced gadgets, and buying new cars.

One thing that I do know to be true: whatever is true in *your* world becomes your reality. This can be dangerous. What should you do? Maybe you should stop watching the news. It won't make you any smarter. Instead, it will make you more fearful, angry, depressed, and hopeless about the future.

In order to complete this exercise, please take the time to answer these questions:

1) When was the last time you watched the news or read a newspaper?

2) In watching the news or reading the newspaper, can you recall any single story that could possibly benefit you either now or in the future? If so, please indicate the news story. If not, please answer by stating that you could not.

3) Why do you watch the news? Be honest. Are you addicted to the negativity as most people are? Does it comfort you to know that some people are worse off than you are? Do you honestly believe that the media is giving you real information that is directly important to your life? If so, please specify how the news assists you in your day to day living to the point of making a significant difference that overpowers the need to ditch the negativity if you ever hope to see success in your life.

Exercise #3
Where Are You?

How old are you? Where are you at this stage of your life? Are you preparing to take over the world as someone in their 20s with positivity and hope in your eyes? Or are you looking forward to retiring soon but maybe you realize that's just not a possibility for you…and perhaps you are disappointed? Are you in your 30s or 40s and realize that if you don't do something else other than working your way up the corporate ladder that you may end up where your parents are? Broke after having lost all of their savings and retirement?

I speak to hundreds of students every year. I can separate most people into two groups: get-rich-quick junkies or Baby Boomers who aren't in the financial place in their life where they thought they should be by now.

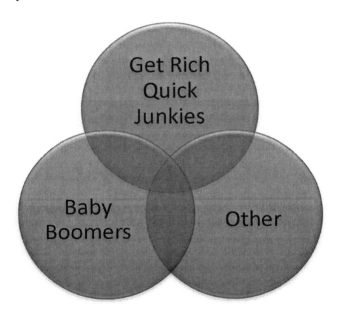

Of course not everyone fits into the get-rich-quick junkie or Baby Boomer group. I get attorneys, engineers, doctors, dentists, and other executives who are unhappy with their line of work or they understand the value of building a passive income if they hope to retire. Many executives and professionals now realize that there is a strong likelihood that they will be working until the day they die; they realize the need for a passive income source and real estate is the *only* solid method of making that happen.

I also get a number of middle-aged men and women who make good money but they didn't apply their high paychecks into any means of investment. They wake up one day, realize that 10 or 20 years whizzed by, and they don't have a single thing to show for it except for piles of accumulated and unwanted debt. This is about when they realize that if they don't change their path, retirement will not happen.

Please complete this exercise by answering the following questions:

1) How old are you?

2) Why now are you deciding to make the financial change by getting involved in real estate investing?

3) How much have you already done in getting a real estate investing education? Have you purchased other courses, attended seminars, and/or read books on the topic? If so, indicate what you have done to start your real estate investing education.

4) Do you understand the value of getting involved in "hang-on" passive income real estate such as residential-commercial or commercial over flipping or buying single-family homes?

Exercise #4
Opportunities Abound

There are a lot of opportunities to be had for making money. You may have been exposed to some and not others. You may be an opportunity junkie who has run the gamut over different opportunities out there. You may be a professional or executive who has made a lot of money in your profession but don't have much in investments or savings to show for it. Maybe all you know is what your investment broker has introduced you to (and I'm sure the results have been unsatisfactory thus far).

Before you can be a successful real estate investor, you need to convince yourself that this is truly the best opportunity for you. Now, I'm not saying that this is the best opportunity for everyone in the world because it's not. Real estate investing is definitely *not* for everyone. I'm not the type of person who is trying to "sell" everyone on the idea that passive income real estate is the ideal opportunity for everyone. My only concern is this: is this opportunity for *you*? If so, how do you know that it's for you?

Take the time to answer these questions in order to show yourself that you are ready to do this:

1) Why do you think that passive income real estate investing fits your personality style? Please describe why.

2) Do you understand that sometimes real estate investing isn't easy? If so, why do you have what it takes to weather through and push past the difficulties that this type of investing may prove to be for you?

3) Describe your personality in 5 words or less.

4) What other opportunities have you had experience with? What other business opportunities or investments have you dealt with? What were the results of those activities?

5) Why do you believe that residential-commercial or commercial real estate investing is the best passive income opportunity around above any other type of business or investment?

6) Do you believe that you have what it takes to make it as a successful real estate investor? If so, please indicate why you are confident that you can make this opportunity work for you.

Exercise #5
Do You Like Real Estate?

Do you like real estate? When you think of real estate, what thoughts cross your mind? I want to make sure that you like what you are getting into. It's pointless to begin if you dislike the idea of owning hundreds of rental units or buying and selling property. In order to get an idea of whether you should pursue this business on a serious level, you need to ask yourself some questions.

Please ask yourself the following questions:

1) When you think about the term "real estate investing," what immediately comes into your mind?

2) What do you like about the idea of becoming a successful real estate investor? What do you dislike about it?

3) Does the idea of having a lot of responsibility in managing and overseeing rental units bother you? If so, why?

4) If you dislike the idea of managing property, have you thought about the alternative of having others manage for you? Do you like or dislike the idea of others managing you properties, especially if you plan on investing out of state?

5) Do you like the idea of having long-term "hang-on" property where you keep your passive income investments for several decades…or forever? If not, please indicate why you don't like this idea.

6) Have you considered that perhaps if having long-term real estate investments may not be your suitable investing choice then maybe you could consider other types of investing such as rehabbing, leasing up units, and then selling within 1 – 3 years?

Exercise #6
Window of Opportunity – It's Closing Fast!

Since so many things are changing in the economy, it's important that you understand that you need to move forward quickly if you want to get the best deals. I have spoken to thousands of students over the past several years and I still get people telling me that they are kicking themselves for not investing in the 1970s. While I was born in the mid-70s, I don't see the value in continuing to cry over spilled milk. The 1970s are over and they're not coming back. Since this is the case, there is no way you can rewind back to 1971 in order to start taking advantage of the real estate opportunities again.

Even though the 1970s aren't ever coming back, nor is the *Great Depression*, it doesn't mean that you missed out on all the good deals. In fact, quite the contrary; for example, I picked up a bank-owned foreclosure last month for about 50% *less* than the amount that the lender had loaned to the former owner back in 1986. Assuming that the former owner had put about 20% cash down and the mortgage didn't reflect the entire asking price in 1986 then this means I got the property for…well, a 1970s-*ish* price. Not bad!

Deals are everywhere but the window of opportunity is closing. If you are waiting around, *stop it!* You can't drag your feet during a time that is prevalent in opportunity. Waiting will only put you in the position of whining later about how you "should have" got in back in 2010/2011 when all the good deals were to be had. My prediction is that by the end of 2011 the economy will begin slowly "thawing" out and starting the pivotal "turn-around" point. The latest you will be able to *possibly* get some good real estate deals will be early 2012, although I'm certain that you will have missed out on a lot of opportunity by then.

Of course, no matter what, there are always opportunities to be had. However, just because this is the case doesn't mean you should drag your feet.

I remember when I got pregnant with my daughter. I was 34 and I didn't feel prepared. Even though I was set mentally, emotionally, and financially, I still didn't feel ready. People left and right all told me the same thing: "No one is every ready to have a baby."

No one is every ready to start investing…or doing *anything* that requires them to push past their comfort zone. Don't be afraid that you may not know everyone or be fully prepared to do this. You will learn as you go in a hands-on fashion.

Let's do a self-assessment:

1) Have you ever kicked yourself for missing out on an opportunity? If so, please explain.

2) Do you understand the reason you should get started now rather than waiting for another year or two because of not being prepared, not having enough money, or any other excuse you may have? If not then please explain why your excuses can validate further delay in action.

3) What do you feel you are lacking in knowledge that will stop you from getting started in residential-commercial or commercial real estate investing right now? How can you bolster that lacking knowledge so you can start investing right away?

4) What scares you the most about moving forward? Please explain.

Exercise #7
What Are Your Goals?

Goal-setting has its limitations. I don't put a lot of stake in goal-setting without flexibility. However, I do notice that each year when I write out my goals, most of them come true even though I bury my goal list at the bottom of a drawer. When I find them again, I realize that most or, in some years, all of my goals have come to fruition. The years that I don't write out a goal list makes me feel as if not as much could have been accomplished if I had.

One thing I like to warn people about is not to make goals grandiose or impossible to achieve. This is one of the elements that self-help authors rarely ever touch upon. It doesn't serve you to set a goal that is so high, you'll never reach it nor have the motivation to because you don't think it's possible to happen. It's best to start out with realistic and attainable goals then "stair step" your way upwards to higher and higher levels with baby steps.

Please answer these important questions:

1) What is amount of "cash flow" are you used to making now based on what you have made, on average, each month for the past couple of years?

2) What amount of money do you need each month to comfortably cover your basic monthly expenses?

3) Within the next 24 months, what would you like your monthly passive income to be?

4) What do you plan on doing within the next 30 days to start the process of reaching your monthly cash flow income as you had indicated above?

Exercise #8
What Are Your Resources?

Everyone has resources, whether they want to believe it or not. Now is the time for you to evaluate those resources to figure out the best action plan for you to implement. These can be people who you wouldn't otherwise consider as resources. It can be a matter of having an 800 FICO on your credit report. It can be the $100,000 equity you have in your home. Don't assume you have no resources because everyone has opportunity inside or outside of themselves that they can use to immediately monopolize upon.

Please answer these questions:

1) Do you have any "talents" that you would be able to use as a successful real estate investor? These talents can be in the following areas:

     a. Property management
     b. People management
     c. Contracting and/or property rehab
     d. Sales/people skills
     e. Writing ability for grants and/or business plans
     f. Negotiation skills
     g. Other (please specify)

2) Do you live in an area of the country that is a "hot" real estate market? (This is an unfair question at this stage in the game because we will be determining what is "hot" as we move forward in this workbook. Consider coming back to this question later if you haven't taken any of my one-on-one mentorship groups yet.)

3) Do you have any cash available to you? If so, indicate how much. **BE HONEST!!** (Don't say you have "nothing" when you have something somewhere.) This can include savings accounts, checking accounts, CDs, home equity, 401K funds, stocks or mutual funds, or change you can suck out of your living room sofa. Indicate what you can get your hands on for cash within 30 – 60 days and don't forget about what your Star Trek collection may be worth by selling your collectibles (or other stuff) on eBay or jewelry that you wouldn't mind selling.

4) Do you have anyone in your family (parents, siblings, offspring, cousins, etc.) who has money (even a small amount) that they may be interested in putting into a solid streamlined investment provided that you can offer up a strong business plan on a specific property deal for them to view? If so, please list these people. You may also include friends, co-workers, associates, or other people who may fit the bill. Indicate how much you think they may have in cash (or other financial resources) for possible real estate deals.

5) What is your average "middle" credit score? If you don't know offhand, you may want to visit **www.Experian.com** and order all 3 of your credit reports to also include a FICO score (and *not* a "power" score) for a definite answer. Do you have any recent bankruptcies or foreclosures in the past 5 years or less? Do you have any recent mortgage "lates" (or late mortgage payments) over the past 3 years?

6) Do you know of anyone (friends, family, spouse, adult child, etc.) who has really good credit? If so, please list these individuals and what you think the condition of their credit may be (based on inadvertent past conversations). Do you think these people may be interested in "partnering" with you on a deal if you personally have poor credit provided that you can convince them that you have a solid real estate deal?

7) List other resources that you have that describe your overall personality and "being" that can be a great attribute to your future success. These may include the following:

     a. Positive attitude
     b. No fear of failure
     c. Action-taker
     d. Self-starter
     e. Persistent
     f. Focused on a single goal
     g. Follow-through
     h. Goal-setter
     i. Other (please specify)

Exercise #9
Willingness

In order to be successful in a serious cash flow business, you have to have an extremely high level of unbreakable commitment. This is not a matter of signing up for an MLM scheme just to find that you don't like it in a few weeks; then you find yourself hopping onto another fly-by-night scam that you also don't like or take seriously and you quickly lose interest yet again. If this is the type of person you are, let me make a "tough-love" suggestion that you not bother with real estate investing until you decide to commit; investing isn't always easy and it's understandable why anyone may want to throw in the towel when the going gets rough.

What are you willing to do to become a successful investor? What are you not willing to do? Everyone has boundaries. Some should be respected. Others just highlight unnecessary laziness or lack of motivation for this type of business. You need to decide where you stand before we start hitting the serious business-building techniques in this workbook.

Please answer these questions:

1) If you are lacking in some area of resource (cash, credit, communication skills, negotiation skills, etc.), are you willing to go out of your way to fix your problems in those areas?

❑   Yes   ❑   No

2) If you are lacking in personal credit, are you willing to work on fixing your bad credit with consistent once-monthly action on each of your 3 credit reports until all of the negative marks have been removed?

❑   Yes   ❑   No

3) Are you willing to take the steps to build business credit in order to bolster your chances of getting a commercial mortgage of a high dollar amount while enjoying the lowest possible interest rate?

❑   Yes   ❑   No

4) If you are lacking in cash, are you willing to use other assets to get some cash together such as selling memorabilia, selling CDs, taking home equity, tapping into your 401K, etc.?

❑   Yes   ❑   No

5) Are you willing to take advantage or bird-dogging or property scouting for other investors to raise money for your own property deals?

❑   Yes   ❑   No

Exercise #10
Understanding Basic Terms

It's time to test some of your basic knowledge so far. I want to make sure you understand some of the basic terminology that has been introduced in *Apartment Building Millionaire* from Chapter 1 through Chapter 4.

Please answer these questions based on the materials located in the book in the chapters specified above:

1) Rental housing is in much higher demand and will continue to be because of which reasons?

2) Real estate investing is not a get-rich-quick scheme. It's a _____ business.

3) If celebrities and sports stars put a minimal percentage of their earnings into investment property, what would be the result of their financial status long after they stop working?

4) Why is it important to do a self-evaluation of your personal finances, FICO (credit report) score, and communication skills?

5) Why is it important to analyze your exact monthly financial requirements to sustain your current lifestyle versus simply choosing a pie-in-the-sky monthly cash flow amount you would like to ultimately see?

6) Apartment building investing is not simply "commercial" real estate but it's considered _____-commercial real estate.

7) Apartment buildings have to have _____ units or more to be considered "commercial" otherwise they fall into the residential category.

8) Do you believe that it's possible to get started in residential-commercial investing with no cash and no credit?

9) Why are "cash flow" investments much more valuable than "flipping" can be?

10) The beauty of getting a commercial loan through a conventional lender is that they don't solely base the their lending decisions on your credit score but rather the property's cash flow; being that this is the case, why do lenders pull your personal credit reports?

11) While fixing your personal credit, you can also start building _____ credit to bolster your chances of getting a better commercial loan with a lower fixed interest rate.

12) If English is your second language or if you don't communicate well with others because of being introverted, what would be your best strategy to overcome this obstacle?

13) Dealing with real estate agents/brokers can be difficult. What is *one thing* you should say if an agent or broker asks you how much money you plan on putting down on the real estate deal you are inquiring about?

14) When you are interested in a property deal and you are ready to move forward but you want to use a creative financing method, should you broach the subject verbally with the listing agent or seller? If so, explain. *If not, why not and what should you do instead?*

15) During economically depressed times, it's best to buy property at rock-bottom prices with the intent on hanging onto them forever. The best time to consider *flipping* property is in a _____ real estate market.

16) What is "hang-on" property and how is this important in your real estate investing business?

17) The "short" word for *rehabilitation* is _____.

Part II:
BUYING PROPERTY

Exercise #11
Finding Your "Farm" Area

This is an important exercise because we begin delving into the nitty-gritty you need to get started investing in real estate deals. Most investors want to rush off into some other state without first considering the state they currently reside in right now. I'm going to lead you through the process of finding your perfect "farm" area to start looking for lucrative real estate deals. You may find that your first attempt at locating profitable properties will be unsuccessful. Do not worry. You will simply return to this exercise and locate another farm area over and over again until you hit your goldmine. (And you *will* eventually hit a goldmine!)

You will be doing an exercise to identify where you live now with a marker dot. If you plan on moving to a new area in the country within the next 12 months, mark that city with a dot as well. Take a thinner marker tipped pen, a pencil, or a regular pen and draw a circle around the dot representing your current residential area. Make your circles anywhere from a 50 to 100 mile radius; draw 5 – 7 circles.

Here's an example that represents me to give you an idea of what you should be doing:

From the results of my circle drawing, you can see that the circles get larger and larger. My initial assessment would tell me to focus in on these areas in this loose order starting first with the immediate city where I live:

1) Valencia, California
2) Los Angeles, California
3) Ventura, California
4) Santa Barbara, California
5) San Bernardino, California
6) Riverside, California,
7) Orange County, California
8) San Diego, California
9) Bakersfield, California
10) Las Vegas, Nevada
11) Fresno, California
12) Reno, Nevada
13) Phoenix, Arizona
14) Oakland, California
15) San Francisco, California
16) Flagstaff, Arizona
17) Sacramento, California
18) Salt Lake City, Utah

The list is, of course, much more detailed since there are a number of major cities in California alone that I missed in this initial assessment. However, I was sticking to the largest cities or counties rather than singularly listing each city.

If you know anything about California, you'll know that there are major cities back to back. In Orange County alone you have dozens of major cities just in the north, central, and south portions of the county. This, of course, doesn't apply to every state of the country but if you are dealing with a state that has a ton of major cities, you can do your analysis by sticking only with the largest cities rather than "secondary suburban" cities with large populations.

For example, if my analysis was based from Panama City, Florida I would start drawing circles to encompass a broader range of large cities and my analysis may look like the following list:

1) Panama City, Florida
2) Pensacola, Florida
3) Mobile, Alabama
4) Tallahassee, Florida
5) Jacksonville, Florida
6) St. Petersburg/Tampa, Florida
7) Montgomery, Alabama
8) Orlando, Florida
9) Birmingham, Alabama
10) Atlanta, Georgia

As you can see, I didn't include other cities that have a larger population but are "small" by the state standards such as Destin, Florida and Dothan, Alabama, for example. This is not to say that these areas hold no significant value in farming out your first property deals. At this stage in the game, you are trying to get an overview analysis of what areas you can work with.

My advice to you is to stick with the major cities because this will make it much easier for you to get conventional funding from a lender. Many lenders have gotten so strict that, unless the city population is 250,000 or more, it will be difficult (or impossible) to get your deal funded. I don't want to see you stuck in a situation where you have busted your buns getting a deal to the point of contract then escrow just to find that you can't get the deal funded.

Now it's your turn to start analyzing the United States to farm deals. If you live outside of the United States and reside in Canada, for example, I still recommend you find and invest in property deals here because they are much more profitable than what you can get where you are now. Since the U.S. economy has suffered a major blow, you may as well take advantage of the rock-bottom prices in our real estate market just as well as anyone else. Canadians should start their property search in the same manner; you should start with where you are and begin drawing circle rings until you hit some major U.S. cities in which to start your investing business.

Now it's your turn. First, create a dot to represent where you live now. If you plan on moving in 12 months or less, create a second dot in that city as well. Begin drawing your circle rings as I instructed in my map on the previous page.

Complete the exercise now on the map below:

1) Draw your dot(s) and circle rings now.

2) Create a list of 5 to 10 major cities that your circle rings hit in the exercise. Create your list of major cities starting with your local city (even if you live in a small town). Every city listed from #2 and beyond should consist of larger cities that have a minimum population of 250,000 residents and above. (You can determine the population demographics by going to **www.uscensusbureau.gov**.)

3) Does your local city (listed as #1) provide enough residents in population to become a possibility as your first "farm" area for property deals? If not, how solid is #2 that you have listed? Please go to www.uscensusbureau.gov or a website for the local city to determine what the population count is and write down your findings to help you with your decision.

4) There are some "trouble" spots in the United States that do not allow for profitable real estate investing at this time. Those spots would be extremely depressed areas such as Detroit, Michigan, Memphis, Tennessee, or Phoenix, Arizona. You wouldn't know off the bat how depressed the area is. However, you should know some information about your local city and the unemployment rate (and if it's above or below the national average). Do you believe that the list of your #1 and #2 cities consists of "depressed" areas? (If you don't know, that's okay. We'll work on the next exercise to help you make that determination.)

Exercise #12
Narrowing Down Your Choices

Now that you've been able to select and start the process of researching a handful of areas of the country, now it's time to do some further research to really narrow down your initial "farming" area. You don't want to spread yourself to thin, especially in the beginning. You want to select 1 or 2 strong areas of the country that (ideally) are very close together. In this exercise you are going to learn how to narrow down your choices by doing some very basic research. These are the same steps you will take time and time again. Every time you start the process of researching a new area, you will begin with this same precise step in this exercise.

You will need an Internet connection. Your first step is to visit **www.LoopNet.com**. You will sign up for a free account if you haven't already. If you want to be a "serious" investor who has access to all of the MLS listings available through this service, it's recommended that you sign up for the *Premium Subscription* which costs less than $150 per quarter. It may seem like a lot of money when you are first getting started but you can't expect to get far in this business if you don't get some basic "supplies" in order to maximize your early success in this business. Just like a new business owner needs office supplies, subscriptions, a phone line, an Internet account, and many other basic necessities, you can't expect to start any kind of business without putting in a few dollars here and there to ensure your success.

If you don't want to get the *Premium Subscription* until you really start to settle into your new position as a real estate investor then that's fine. However, please be aware that you won't have access to a good portion of the MLS through LoopNet.com without purchasing the upgrade.

Let's get started.

Please complete this assignment by answering the following questions:

1) Visit **www.LoopNet.com** and sign up for a free basic subscription or *a Premium Subscription* (depending on how serious you feel right now as a real estate investor). Begin by doing a search for "multifamily" ONLY (having only that box checked) and then type in the complete city and state, starting with the first one on your list from the previous exercise. Sort the properties by "CAP" rate (highest to lowest). Quickly sift past the mobile home parks and ANY property that has less than 5 units. Count how many properties are left and write down the number below.

---

2) Now that you have the number of properties that are left (less the mobile home parks and duplexes, triplexes, and "quads"), take a calculator and add up each CAP rate listed in the listings presented. If there are 10 properties, you should have 10 separate CAP rates (unless there isn't one listed; this may be the case for vacant properties). If you find ANY property that doesn't have a listed CAP, delete it out from the amount of properties you have left. If there initially were 10 properties then now there are only 9 counted. Add up ALL the properties that have a CAP rate listed and write the total number below. Note: for the most ACCURATE assessment, take the LOWEST CAP RATE listed and *drop it out* of the equation. So, if you have 9 properties and you drop the lowest CAP rate then reduce your amount of properties to 8.

_____

3) You will work the following basic math equation:

Average CAP Rate _____ / (Divided Into) _____ Total # of Properties = _____

For example: if you had 10 properties with CAP rates and the total between all 10 was 76 then you would punch in the number 76 into your calculator, then the DIVIDE (or forward slash) sign and punch in your number of units or 10 then press the EQUAL key getting the answer of 7.6. Your average CAP rate would be 7.6%.

4) What is your average CAP rate in your first area?

_____

5) If the average CAP rate for the area is 8% or below then your area will not allow for you to successfully work deals where you are coming in with no cash and no credit. Therefore, you will have to scrap your first selected city/state on your list and move onto the next one. Did your average CAP rate drop below the 8%?

      ❑   Yes   ❑   No

6) Please work through the rest of your selected areas even if you did find your first area that meets the 8% or above CAP rate criterion. Make a listing of each city/state below and list the average CAP rate you had calculated next to each. It's important that you do this now and perhaps do it again in 6 months then again in 12 months. If an area is "ripe" for acquisition, you'll notice the CAP rates beginning to drop, even if it's a minor drop of a portion of 1%. List each city/state below and put the average CAP rate next to it, then date the bottom of this page so you can work the same exercises in the future to make a comparison later when you do this research project again.

Exercise #13
Selecting Your Farm Area

I'm now going to assume that you have found a ripe area for the pickings with the exercise you had completed in the previous exercise. If you did not find a "ripe" area then keep move out with your circles until you hit a major city that has a higher than 8% CAP rate average. Also, sometimes an area will have a listed property or two that will "throw" the balance of your averages. If the properties are way below the "eyeball" average then throw them both out of the equation. Here is an example:

Asking Price	Number of Units	CAP Rate
$1,200,000	52	7.6%
$1,900,000	70	8.7%
$900,000	38	5.7%
$430,000	12	7.9%
$985,000	42	7.9%
$2,300,000	98	8.1%
$3,200,000	130	9.1%

You can see from the sample chart above than there is one "oddball" CAP rate of 5.7% that doesn't "fit in" with an eyeball view of what the others look like. If you have more than 1 "oddball" low CAP rate then throw it out.

Of course, if you notice an "oddball" high CAP rate then you would only be doing yourself a service by throwing that one out as well. Typically if a listing agent lists a multifamily property over 12% then he is basing his numbers on "proforma" rather than "actual" numbers. About 99% of the time when this happens you will find that the property is completely vacant and he is basing his figures on if you came in with 100% cash and what you *could* get if you were to lease up the building in the future to a 95% occupancy at usually an unrealistically high rental price per unit. Take note of these unusually high CAP rates and throw those out as well.

Going back into LoopNet.com for this exercise, I want you to work through these questions:

1) Choose your "top" 3 areas that you are really cheering for regardless of the reason. It can be because it's where you live or where you plan on moving. Write each of the 3 cities and states below in a list, starting with your most preferred and ending with your lease preferred:

      1. _____

      2. _____

      3. _____

2) You will do a separate LoopNet.com search for EACH of the cities listed above. By looking at all of the MLS listings that are in the "multifamily" category of being 5 or more units and losing the mobile home parks out, what is the average "eyeball" CAP rate that you can tell just by scanning your eyes over the properties that have the CAP rates listed in the cities you have listed in order:

    1. _____

    2. _____

    3. _____

3) Does your "eyeball" analysis allow you to exceed your average 8% (or higher) CAP rate needed to make each of your 3 listed areas? Indicate which cities allow for the 8%+ CAP and which do not.

4) Write down the city or cities that meet the 8%+ CAP rate "eyeball" test below. If you don't have any listed then you will have to go back and move out with your circles a little farther until you can list at least 1 city/state below. If you have more than 1 city/state, list them below but not to exceed a total of 3.

_____

_____

_____

Exercise #14
Hitting the Pavement

Let's start looking at properties to buy. This exercise will require that you have an Internet connection and preferably a printer. Using the website **www.LoopNet.com** you will begin searching for properties in the commercial MLS. If you want to use other sites like **www.CIMLS.com** or **www.CoStar.com** then you may. I will tell you that all the sites have the same listings pulled from the same database but some of the platforms may be more user friendly than others and more suitable for your personal preferences.

Log into the site and you will begin looking at property from your selected farm area, starting with your most preferred city/state listed (and probably the city/state closest to home for you).

Please complete these exercises:

1) Look through the MLS and search for "multifamily" properties that are 5 units or more. You want to skip past the duplexes, triplexes, and "quads." You also want to skip past the mobile home parks for right now. As a new investor your "limit" cannot exceed $4.5 million in asking price. (Mind you, the price will be chewed down in the negotiation process.) For the purposes of your loan, the financed amount by the conventional funder needs to exceed $1 million in order to have a commercial lender want to fund the deal (otherwise you are dealing with "hybrid" residential and commercial properties; thus they look closely at personal credit and income unlike commercial lenders who look at property cash flow). In order to get a conventional loan, the occupancy needs to be at or above 85%. Assumable loans are difficult to acquire unless the seller is "distressed" or behind on mortgage payments so avoid those deals as well. Analyze your deals based on the following list:

    1.   85% occupancy or above
    2.   Asking price not to exceed $4.5 million
    3.   Final offer price not to drop below $1.25 million
    4.   No assumable loan
    5.   Listed CAP rate to exceed 8% (even better if it's 9%+)

How many properties fall into the above criteria? _____

2) List the properties by address, asking price, and other relevant information below. It's recommended that you print out each one for future use. If there is a flyer attached, print that too. Submit an online inquiry to the listing agent through the LoopNet.com system if you are using their service. You will do this for each of your selected areas if you have chosen more than 1 to work with.

3) By automatically shaving off between 10% and 15% of the asking price (or an "average" of 12.5%), will each property still fit the criteria? You don't want your "financed" amount to drop below $1 million or exceed $4 million. If using a conventional funding source, you can get "up to" an 85% LTV on a loan. Therefore, a $1.25 million property that you "shave" down to $1,093,750. Using the 85% LTV figure, your loan amount will be $939,687.50. This, of course, is below the required $1 million. Take each of your property deals, shave off 12.5% of the asking price, and then calculate your conventional loan at an 85% LTV. Would the funded amount be equal to or greater than $1 million for each deal? Please list the results below:

4) List your deals that fit all of the criteria (as far as you know; sometimes "assumable loan" information is not immediately available on the MLS listing). Do this for each of your farm areas.

Exercise #15
Get More Information

For some reason, this is the part that stops people in their tracks. They have a fear of calling brokers, real estate agents, and sellers for fear that they will sound stupid or unprofessional. I hate to break it to you but in the beginning you will sound a little "green" but that will quickly pass the faster you call as many agents and sellers as possible.

To simplify the process, contact listing agents by way of email first. LoopNet.com makes this easy for you. They have a means of allowing interested investors to submit an online query on a property with a single click of a button. Make sure you are asking for "actual income and expenses" on all of your property inquiries. Never settle for "proforma" numbers because they do not reflect the reality of the property's current profit/loss. Instead they are "pie-in-the-sky" numbers of how the property *may* be able to perform sometime in the future and those numbers are worthless.

Your job now is to get the "actual" income and expenses on the property deals you have found so far. First submit your Internet inquiry and see what happens. If they do not respond in a day or two then follow up with a phone call. You will find that many real estate agents are lazy, unresponsive, and are terrible at contact with prospects. You may wonder how they make a living. Many don't do very well financially. Some thrive off their one sale per year that exceeds several million dollars for a nice 3% commission and that carries them through the rest of the year as they bask away on the beach and cherry pick the deals that they *may* want to do.

Please complete these exercises:

1) Start inquiring on your property deals. Ask for actual income and expenses. If the broker begins to probe about you, your experience, and how much money you will be putting down, give as little information as possible. Be sure to have a standard answer to the down payment question. Your answer should always be as follows: "I'll put down whatever it takes to make the deal happen." And leave it at that! Submit an online inquiry on each of your properties of interest. Then follow up with a phone call for each one. Report your results below:

2) When you talked to the listing agent on the phone, what questions or comments did you find that stumped you? Did you find that he (or she) was abrasive, rude, and uncaring? Did you find that you dislike who you dealt with? (If you find someone you like and have a rapport with who is willing to help you then you hit pay dirt!)

3) Were you able to get the actual income and expenses on your properties of interest? Did the broker/agent send you a "package" to include a rent roll, property pictures, and a business plan? What did you receive (if anything)?

Exercise #16
Analysis

Y ou need to use the information you received to really dig into your property deal(s) to determine if you should continue on to the next step…or not. You will find that this business is a numbers game that hinges directly on how well you pack your pipeline. You will constantly have to look for new deals, work the numbers, start the pre-due diligence process, and many other steps that may result in a deal that isn't going to work. It will be disappointing to you if you find yourself working on one or two deals per month just to find that they won't work out and then you'll blame your unlucky stars because you aren't making anything happen.

Even experienced investors with money to put down have challenges with deals. We find out at some point in the process that the broker or seller lied about the "actual" income and expenses. The deal cannot progress forward because the property is losing money. Or perhaps they produced a rent roll showing that the property is 90% occupied except that 40% of the tenants hadn't paid rent in 3 months. Perhaps the property is lacking in structural integrity and there is a cracked foundation, a black mold problem, or termites. This may not be revealed until after we go into escrow and start the physical inspection process with a licensed building inspector.

Just understand that this game of real estate is a numbers game. If you are in any business, especially sales, you understand that sometimes there are a lot of sales calls and door-knocking that has to occur before a successful sales is made. You would also understand that sometimes you may get close to a sale just to have it fall through at the last second. This is normal in any business that has a small success rate percentile.

Before continuing on with the process, you will have to do some basic math to see if it's worth going into the next phase. You will take the "actual" income and expense information that was given to you to make an assessment of the property to work out the mathematical details.

Please work through these questions:

1) Take your first property of interest. Have access to the Internet and be prepared to go to this website: **www.mortgage-calc.com**. You will use the simple mortgage calculator option. The average going conventional mortgage for a commercial property is anywhere from 6% to 7.5% on a fixed rate. Take your first property, assume that you can offer 10% off the asking price and assume that you will be financing 100% of the property purchase (even though you won't be from one single lender). Find out what your total "debt service" or mortgage would be by using the website listed below on each of your properties of interest from your list. Debt service is calculated annually. When you get your monthly mortgage rate, multiply the answer by 12 and you then have your annual debt service figure. What is the annual debt service for each of your property deals?

2) You will then take your "net operating expenses" that were given to you by the listing agent (and hopefully they are "actual" and not "proforma" numbers) and add this number to your debt service. If you have tax information, please add the tax figures as well. Taxes are always an estimate and you won't know what the real tax figures are until after the close of escrow when the county assessor reassesses the property. What is your total annual "debt" including expenses, taxes (if available), and debt service?

3) According to the actual numbers that were given to you, what is the Gross Operating Income (GOI) on the property based on the current occupancy rate? This is also calculated annually.

4) Here is your equation:

   Gross Operating Income = _____

   (minus) -

   Net Operating Expenses = _____

   (minus) -

   Debt Service (Mortgage) = _____

   Cash Flow   = _____

What is the cash flow on each of your properties? Is it *positive* or *negative*? For a free version of my CFE, go to **www.FreeCashFlowEvaluator.com**. This will help you calculate your figures.

Exercise #17
What Have You Found?

Remember, this process will be a numbers game for you. You will have to work through a great number of property deals in your farming area to find deals that will work if you are trying to structure the deal without putting any money down. Now, you don't always have to use my "rule of thumb" which is getting a bottom-line cash flow of $25,000 per year per $1 million in asking price. You can cut that figure in half, especially if you find a deal where the property seller is going to offer you a lot of incentives including a huge chunk in partial owner financing or seller carry-back.

When you structure a deal where you assume you aren't going to put any money down, please understand that you will not get a single conventional funding source to give you a 100% LTV or 100% of the funds on the purchase price to close your deal. Those types of loans didn't exist in the heyday of lending and they certainly don't exist now. When you are structuring the deal to assume that 100% of the property will be funded, you will be structuring the deal where multiple parties will be helping the financed portion of the deal. To do a "quick-and-dirty" analysis of the deal, it's simple just to "pretend" that a single source will be giving you a 100% LTV on the deal at a 6.5% fixed interest rate (for example) over a 25-year term. This will not reflect the final financial structure of the deal unless you are doing a lease-option or getting the property 100% financed with the seller acting as a bank.

Through your property analysis, have you been able to locate any profitable residential-commercial deals? If you haven't then you need to keep looking. Understand that you will be dropping the asking price by about 10% to 15% right off the bat since no seller will ever expect to receive full asking price in any market, especially this one. However, if you are finding that you have to drop the price 30% or more to get a cash flow then, chances are, you are in the wrong area of the country. Consider moving on to one of your other cities that showed promise in your research.

Please answer these questions:

1) Have you been able to locate any deals with strong financial potential? If so, please list them below. If not, please indicate the obstacles that you have come across.

2) If you have found lucrative property deals, even getting them structured with zero down, are you prepared to take the next steps (which can be kind of scary)? If you have not found any deals, what is your next step? Please indicate your plans from today and moving forward.

3) How well do you know the area where you are farming deals? Do you know anything about the area, demographics, population size, unemployment rates, etc.? If not, are you willing to proceed by doing some of this basic research next?

Exercise #18
Research and Demographics

It's always nice to know what you are getting yourself into before you make a major step (or mistake) in purchasing property in an area that is going downhill. Some basic Internet research that will take about 30 – 60 minutes will help you determine whether your farming area is worth pursuing…or not!

I have students ask me daily which areas of the country are good and which ones are not good for investing purposes. My difficulty comes in when I have to base my advice on different partnership or property scout deals that have come in; this allows me the benefit of seeing a broad cross-section of the entire U.S. without doing any of the research myself.

I personally only invest in a small handful of areas, mostly in Florida and in the south. I do not invest in "cold" areas (because heating costs drive up operating expenses). I do not spread myself too thin, even being the "expert" that I am. No one should have tons of property in too many places around the country anyway because it is a recipe for a disaster called *losing control*.

Everyone, especially beginning investors, should stick with one area and purchase a whole bunch of properties there first before venturing off into another city. Even then your new city should be close by your other acquired properties or become a new area that you plan on solely purchasing another boatload of properties before considering moving on. No investor should have property in more than 5 different central places in the country; by "central" I'm referring to the "greater" part of an area. For example, if you are purchasing property in Orlando and then decide to start buying property in Jacksonville, this would be part of a single "greater" area even though technically they are 2 very different cities. However, if you are purchasing property in Orlando then start purchasing in Birmingham, Alabama then this would be considered a separate area where you may take on other surrounding major Alabama cities (and have them still be considered part of the same "greater" area).

Your next step in your area is to assess its value. Places like Detroit, Michigan may offer a lot of "opportunity" but you can't invest in an area where no one wants to live or can find jobs to pay the rent. I had a student argue with me on the phone about Detroit and how much opportunity is there. I told him that I don't agree because if you can't get renters to pay rent then you are done before you started. He went on and on about how cheap the properties are. I said, "Fine, but do you have 100% cash for all of the deals? If not, no one will give you a dime in financing for that area." That seemed to shut him up.

Any area that is dependent upon a single industry (i.e. Detroit with American car manufacturing) is not a good property farming area. The "rust belt" areas of the country like Pennsylvania, Ohio, and Indiana are in trouble as they lose good chunks of their population on an annual basis. These also would not be good investment areas (unless something changes, of course).

Be very aware of what is going on with your farming area. Any area that is losing population each year does *not* have opportunity. Any area that has a higher-than-national-average unemployment rate is *not* a good area to invest. Any area that sees high property vacancy rates (below 75% occupied as an average) *isn't* a great property investment area.

You can start your research by going to **www.USCensusBureau.us** to find database information on city and state populations. You can visit the city to see what kind of demographics and population information it can provide. You can do a Google.com search on the city's unemployment rate then compare it to the national average. This is all easy stuff to do if you have a lazy Saturday afternoon and really want to make sure that you are going into the right area…or not. Now is the time to figure that out.

My students who are on my email blast lists get critical information from me on the status of different areas of the country and which markets are hot or not. Last year I did a blast about how Phoenix, Arizona was having problems because it was overbuilt and there was a Sheriff in town who was taking great strides to get rid of illegal immigrants. (This would be almost one year before this immigration issue exploded on national media.) The other problem was that apartment building owners and employers were getting fined for having anything to do with offering rentals or employment to illegal immigrants. This is what drove out a good percentage of the population in Phoenix and the average occupancy percentage dropped to about 50%. *Not good!*

I did the blast and most people are very appreciative of the important and valuable information I routinely provide. There are, of course, some jerks in the group that never appreciate anything or have rude comments for the information I provide.

I recently did such a blast about the Florida real estate market simply stating that all lenders have pulled back to only provide a maximum LTV of 65% on all Florida real estate deals. This means that an investor would have to come in with 35% cash down. *No exceptions.* Upon sending out that blast I had my usual jerk send me an email saying that I am "such a negative person" because he successfully was able to purchase a Phoenix property (purposely defying my recommendation to stay away from Phoenix in my last warning email). He then complained that he purchased this wonderful property and couldn't find a single person to rent his new units to, even after dumping money into cosmetic upgrades and light rehab. His complaint made me scratch my head. I *warned* him about Phoenix and yet he took the jump anyway after reading my warning. Then he *blamed* me for being "negative." I think he thought that because I warned people, I must be the one responsible for *souring* a local economy because of my negative "vibes" or something. People are weirdoes sometimes. Damned if you do, damned if you don't!

Start doing research and then answer these questions:

1) Find the total population of ALL of the cities you have on your list from the prior exercise of locating your farm areas. Please list each city and its total population.

2) Find the current national unemployment rate. What is the percentage? Please write it below.

_____

3) Find the unemployment rates for each of your potential farming cities. What is the percentage of each? Write down the city name and the percentage next to it. Write down "lower" or "higher" if it's lower or higher than the national average as you indicated above.

4) Find the percentage of lost or gained population in the last year. Go back for the last 5 years total. List each of your selected cities and indicate the population starting 5 years back and working up to last year. Has your city been gaining or losing population consistently? What is the average percentage or gain (or loss) for each of your selected cities? You can even go back 10 years if you wish for more thorough analysis.

5) List the major industries or companies that dominate each of your chosen areas. Is each city comprised of a single industry or company, or are there several? Make this assessment by doing some online research and write down what you have found below.

6) Here is your opportunity for a final "yes" or "no" on your area. Remember, this can change at any time and if you believe you have a city that has potential later, you can do this exercise again next year or the year after. List each city and, based on your research above, say "yes" or "no" to indicate if you found positive news or negative news about your areas.

Exercise #19
Structuring Financing

It will be instrumental in your success to understand how to structure financing. OPM or Other People's Money is what real estate investing is all about. The faster you come to understand how you will have to structure your deals, the better. You will get good at doing this the more times you analyze each serious deal you have.

I am going to go through allowing you to structure several types of deals in order to give you a good understanding of how each will work. I will tell you that I will not have you do structuring analysis or work on lease-option or 100% owner financing deals because they are pretty cut-and-dried. You work something out with the seller at a specific monthly payment or asking price then you put together a private mortgage contract. End of story.

The creativity comes in when you have to use conventional funding and other financing resources so that you can actually get into a deal where you put nothing down.

Work through these exercises the best you can:

1) Pretend that your property deal is $2,000,000. You want to get a conventional funder involved at a 75% LTV (which is the typical LTV for most conventional lenders). You want to use seller carry-back but you understand that most lenders will want to see cash in the escrow account as your down payment before they will fund the deal; many lenders will *not* accept seller carry-back (although some rare ones do). For this deal, $500,000 represents 25% of the transaction or the cash down payment needed to make this deal close. Assuming that closing costs will be 7% of the total asking price, how much will you need in closing costs? Assuming that the seller will cover "seller concessions" or appraisals and building inspections, how much total cash will you need to close this deal? (Add up your $500,000 down payment plus closing costs for your answer.)

2) If you chose to use a transactional funder for the down payment and it costs 2.5% of the down payment amount (of the $500,000) then how much extra will you need to cover this cost?

3) If you are forced to get POF or proof of funds from the bank to show that you have the down payment money before the close of escrow, you will need to get this "proof" from a company that provides this service. Assuming the fee is 2% of the $500,000, what is the additional fee needed to cover this? Add all of your fees together. What will you need total including the $500,000, closing costs, transactional funding fees, and POF fees to close on this deal?

4) If you decide to hit the owner up for his or her equity on a "buyer's repair credit," how much will they need to have in equity? (Hint: it's the exact amount you have determined above.)

5) Many times it's hard to get the seller to go with such a high buyer's repair credit. It will be even harder to convince the bank to accept such a transaction. I have a broker who can get an 85% LTV on most deals so you can focus in on getting 15%. If you ask for the seller to pay all closing costs, work the math again and indicate what the difference would be in the needed buyer's repair credit (or owner's equity).

Exercise #20
Hard Money

Hard money is expensive. This should be your last resort. In fact, this will probably make your deal unprofitable in most cases. Hard money is typically done on interest-only terms and at a high interest rate of anywhere from 12% (on the very low end) to 18% (and even higher sometimes).

Many times you can get a hard money lender to cover a "bridge" or short-term loan of anywhere from 6 – 18 months. This may seem like a viable idea when you are struggling to find money to close on a deal. Be careful! Many times it is very difficult to "refinance" your loan into a conventional once after acquisition of the property. If you are "under water" on your hard money loan the second you close escrow, chances are that you'll be facing a foreclosure.

Please work through these questions:

1) By doing a Google.com search for "interest only mortgage calculator," find a calculator that you feel comfortable with. You will also need to work with my favorite online mortgage calculator at **www.Mortgage-Calc.com**. Do the math below and see the differences for yourself. Both properties have an LTV that will be financed at the amount of $1.5 million.

   a. A conventional lender gives you a fixed rate of 5.85% for $1.5 million. Using the mortgage calculator listed at the above URL, what is the annual debt service (or mortgage)? Simply take the answer that is given to you and multiply it by 12.

   b. A hard-money lender gives you an interest-only rate of 15% for $1.5 million. There is no "term" specified but if you must insert a number of years use 25. What is the annual debt service on this loan?

   c. Compare the 2 answers. Do you see the difference?

2) Knowing the difference between the two answers, do you see the value in using hard-money? Do you see how rapidly it can eat up any possible cash flow you may have in a property deal?

Exercise #21
Creating an Offer

I believe in using what is called a "hybrid" LOI/offer form. As you know, an LOI is a Letter of Intent. These are generally used in hot real estate markets to inform a seller of your intent to put in an official legally-binding offer in a specified time frame so, "Hold up on choosing another offer until I get my mind-blowing offer in because here's what I plan on presenting in my real offer..." In a slow real estate market, putting in a traditional LOI is a waste of time because you won't have to compete against multiple offers where an LOI is necessary.

What I like about the LOI is that it is *not* legally binding. If you change your mind 2 minutes after the seller accepts it, you can walk away without any legal recourse. A typical LOI is merely a letter. It doesn't prompt a signature or response from the seller. An offer prompts a signature or response but is legally binding.

My "hybrid" version is the best of both worlds. It offers the non-legally binding nature of an LOI with the offer structure in place to require a response from the seller.

Are you ready to put together an LOI/offer? For this, you will need the following information:

- Listing agent's name, company name, address, and phone number
- The seller's name (which is usually an LLC)
- The property's APN or Assessor's Parcel Number
- The property's total square footage
- The property's total lot size in acres
- Your offer price (which hopefully *isn't* the seller's asking price)
- Information on how you will structure your loan
- Will you be offering an earnest money deposit? (This is typically 2% to 3% of the purchase price. If you don't have it, don't offer it!)

Here is a sample LOI/offer form

September 15, 2010

Monica Main
Main Investment Group LLC
25050 Avenue Kearny, Suite 215
Valencia, CA 91355
(661) 295-5050

Burnstein Realty Inc.
Robert Burnstein
15609 Sea Village Dr., Ste. 105
San Diego, CA 93501
(619) 294-1300

RE: 5015 Myers Road, Union City, CA 93535

BUYER:	**Main Investment Group LLC**
SELLER:	**Myers-Union Building LLC**

PURCHASE PRICE: $2,450,000

PREMISES ADDRESS: 5015 Myers Road, Union City, CA 93535

PREMISES AREA: Approximately 56,885 ± feet of space on approximately 1.2 acre parcel consisting of 4 buildings and a total of 20 units under APN 204-298-1033.

TERMS OF PURCHASE: Buyer to qualify and receive a first-position conventional loan for 85 % of the purchase price or **$2,082,500.** Conventional loan is to be fully amortized over 35 years, not to exceed a 6% fixed interest rate with no pre-payment penalty. Buyer to come in with 15% cash or a total of **$367,500** as a down payment. Asking price is based on appraised value. If appraised value falls below the asking price, Seller is to lower the asking price or terminate the purchase and pay all due diligence costs.

INSPECTION PERIOD: Buyer, at its sole and unfettered discretion, shall be allowed a thirty (30) day period from opening of escrow to review all documentation, obtain third-party reports, and otherwise approve the Property. If Buyer determines that, for any reason, the Property is not suitable for Buyer's use, Buyer's earnest money and any additional funds deposited into escrow by Buyer shall be returned to the Buyer within five (5) business days and neither party shall have any liability or obligation to one another hereunder.

FINANCING PERIOD: Upon waiver of contingencies, Buyer shall have obtained a loan application detailing terms acceptable to Buyer. Buyer, at its sole and unfettered discretion, shall be allowed a forty-five (45) day period from waiver of contingencies to complete the application, provide lender with all documentation, and obtain a loan commitment, at terms the same as indicated above or better or otherwise acceptable to Buyer. If Buyer determines that, for any reason, the loan terms are not acceptable, such purchase agreement shall terminate. Buyers earnest money and any other funds deposited into escrow by the Buyer shall be returned within five (5) business days and neither party shall have any liability or obligation to one another hereunder.

CLOSING DATE: Fifteen (15) days after waiver of contingencies.

OPENING OF ESCROW: Opening of escrow will be the date that signed escrow instructions are received by First American Title Company along with the earnest money deposit.

CONFIDENTIALITY: All aspects of this negotiated agreement shall be held by Buyer and Seller in the strictest of confidence. The confidentiality requirement shall not be in effect once closing occurs.

PRORATION: Taxes, rents, and other income and expenses pertaining to the Property will be prorates as part of the close of escrow.

BROKER: Any principals acting on the behalf of the Buyer are licensed real estate brokers in California and are acting as principals only. Seller shall be responsible for all brokerage commissions.

SELLER'S OBLIGATION: The Seller is required to provide all financial documentation to verify income and expenses on the property within fifteen (15) days after the opening of escrow. The Seller will also pay for appraisals, property inspections, and closing costs. The Seller will authorize a Buyer's Repair Credit not to exceed $500,000 for post-acquisition repairs to be made by Buyer post-closing repairs and/or rehab.

SCOPE OF THIS LETTER: *The Buyer and Seller acknowledge that this proposal is not a legally-binding offer and that it is intended only as the basis for the negotiations of a purchase contract. Accordingly, this proposal does not constitute a legally binding agreement, nor shall there be any binding agreement between the parties unless and until a fully executed purchase contract hand delivered to Seller by Buyer, or Buyer's agent.*

Should the foregoing proposal be acceptable to both parties, a purchase contract will be drafted for both parties review and approval within fifteen (15) days of acceptance. The terms expressed in this Letter of Intent will become null and void if not accepted within seven (7) days from the date of this letter. During this period Seller agrees to discontinue any third-party sale negotiations. **In any event, this proposal shall expire September 22, 2010 at 5 PM Pacific Time.**

_____

Seller   Date

_____

Buyer   Date

Let's get started:

1) Your first portion of your LOI/offer will look like the sample below. Emulate the sample with your own information as best as possible by writing your applicable information right next to or under mine below:

[TODAY'S DATE]

Monica Main
Main Investment Group LLC
25050 Avenue Kearny, Suite 215
Valencia, CA 91355
(661) 295-5050

Joe Blowmower
Blowmower Real Estate Sales
1234 Main Lane, Suite 400
Los Angeles, CA 90012

RE: 1005 8th Street, Los Angeles, CA 90001

Buyer: Main Investment Group LLC

Seller: Eight Street Property LLC

Purchase Price: $1,400,000

Property Description: An **8-unit** residential-commercial property with a total rentable square footage or approximately **10,000 square feet**; parcel consisting of **0.47 acres** under **APN 209-208-1772**.

Terms: Buyer to receive a first-position conventional loan for 85% of the purchase price or **$1,119,000**; fully amortized over 25 years, non-recourse, with no prepayment penalty, interest rate not to exceed 6.5%. Buyer to put down 15% cash or **$210,000**. In the event that the property does not appraise at the purchase price, Seller will lower the price to the appraised value or terminate the contract and/or escrow without financial or legal recourse to the Buyer; Seller will then pay for all due diligence costs to the point of transaction termination.

Earnest Money Deposit: Upon execution of the contract, Buyer will provide an earnest money deposit in the amount of **$42,000** to open escrow. This amount is fully refundable in the event that the contract or escrow phase is terminated at the biding of the Seller or Buyer. *(If you have no earnest money deposit, delete this entire section.)*

Seller's Duties: Seller to allow for a seller concession to cover due diligence costs such as appraisals and building inspections. Seller to pay closing costs. Seller to authorize a Buyer's Repair Credit in an amount not to exceed **$500,000** to pay for post-acquisition repairs and rehab as needed.

Now it's your turn. Type out a rough draft using the template as provided above to write out at least one LOI/offer. If you do not have a serious property deal you are working on right now, find something on LoopNet.com and write out a sample offer anyway just to get a feel for how the processes works.

2) Fill out as many LOI/offers as you have promising deals for. If you are missing information such as the seller's name, APN, or other key information, follow up with the listing agent until you can get the information. It looks unprofessional to have NA or brackets like this in your documentation: [APN] Indicate below how many LOI/offers you have been able to write out for the amount of serious deals you currently have:

_____

3) Do you have earnest money for your deals? If not, please delete out the section in your LOI/offer that makes mention of earnest money. Earnest money is *not* presented in the form of a check at the time of submitting the offer. It's usually presented upon offer acceptance or after the official legal contract has been accepted and the property goes into escrow. This would be the amount that opens up the escrow account. If you do not have earnest money, remove the section from each of your offers. If you do, indicate below how much money you are working with total for earnest money and other due diligence costs:

_____

4) Submit your LOI/offers. Submit *all* of them. No need to wait until each comes back one-by-one as an acceptance or rejection. The nice part about the LOI/offer format is that it is not legally binding and therefore you do not have to follow through with the deal once the seller accepts it. Also, you will not be giving up an earnest money deposit check at the time of submission so you can technically wallpaper your entire town with these LOI/offers and there would be no legal recourse to you. How many LOI/offers have you been able to submit? Indicate this below:

_____

5) Keep a log of the responses on your offers. Usually the negotiation phase happens verbally or via email after your LOI/offer is submitted. Don't expect to get a formal counteroffer back because 99% of the time you'll receive nothing back. Instead you'll either receive a verbal (or email) rejection or instructions on what you *should* change in your LOI/offer to get the seller to accept the deal. A week or two may pass before you hear anything. Constantly follow up. Follow up within 24 hours after the LOI/offer accepted to make sure it's been received. You can submit via fax or email. If you submit via email, be sure to convert your LOI/offer into a PDF file so that the listing agent can't change any details of the document you sent over. Do *not* submit your documents in any type of document that can be changed if you are sending it via email. If you cannot convert your document then you should fax your LOI/offers instead. Follow up again the day before LOI/offer expiration. Give only 7 days for

acceptance before the LOI/offer expires. Don't be surprised when you find out that many of your deals will be accepted or responded to long after the expiration date. This is common. Indicate your progress after 1 week of submitting offers. Out of the amount of offers you submitted, how many came back with a response (positive or negative or with "negotiated" terms)?

———————————

6) One of the things a seller will come back with on your LOI/offer is your specific amount you have listed for the "buyer's repair credit." They will wonder why you know the exact amount that will be needed in repairs when this is usually indicated later in the form of an offer addendum after the building inspector creates a report on the needed property repairs or damage. You then explain that your assets are "tied up" on other deals right now and if they want to close escrow, they will be offering up some of the equity on their property for you to pay back your investor who will be "lending" you the cash down for the close of escrow. You then explain that once the building inspection has been completed, you will be able to better determine exactly the amount of repairs that need to be done on the property after acquisition. If the amount does not meet the requested repair credit amount then the remaining amount can be paid back to the seller *after* you close escrow and a Private Mortgage Contract (PMC) will be put in place to outline the payment plan before you close escrow. (This is also something that the lender will never see and *not* something you want to share with the lender at *any* time.) This is when you'll determine whether they have this amount in equity or if they are willing to proceed with the deal under those terms. You can also let them know that after you close escrow, they can place a second-position lien against the property in the amount of the PMC if they want to feel more secure about the transaction but they have to agree to remove the lien if you want to pull equity out later to cash them out on the second-position loan. (Usually they don't have any problems with this. How many "conversations" such as the one outlined above did you have to have with sellers? (This is typically done verbally. You don't submit another offer but you could offer a "proposed" payment plan on the seller carry-back portion of the deal.) Were any successful? (Don't worry; you'll get better at this as you go along. Practice makes perfect. Don't avoid this task because it feels uncomfortable. Keep pressing forward and it *will* become second nature to you.)

———————————

7) If your first batch of LOI/offers were unsuccessful, put another action plan in place to submit another "batch" out there. This is why this business is a numbers game. Keep packing your deal pipeline full. You want to ideally submit 3 – 5 LOI/offers each week consistently. Do you have next week lined up? If not, start getting some more deals together. Don't wait around to hear from someone on the other LOI/offers you have submitted. Instead, keep submitting more! Outline next week's action plan below:

You shouldn't plan on scaring a property seller away with piles and piles of clauses and contingencies. However, you may want to consider a few of these when it comes to dealing with both the offer and the contract phase (which is next in the process):

ACCEPTANCE OF BACK-UP OFFER. Buyer agrees that this offer is accepted as a back-up offer only and is contingent upon the cancellation of the existing Sales Contract Reference Dated _____ between Seller and _____, by no later than _____ days following the acceptance of this offer as a back-up offer. If the existing Sales Contract is cancelled within said time period, this offer shall become the primary offer. If the existing Sales Contract is not cancelled within said time period, this offer shall become null and void. Buyer reserves the right to declare this offer null and void at any time prior to cancellation of the first offer.

APPRAISAL CONTINGENCY. The Buyer may order and pay for an appraisal on the property. If the appraised value is less than the total purchase price stated in the contract of sale, the Buyer may, within three (3) calendar days of Buyer's receipt of the appraisal, at Buyer's sole option, declare this offer null and void. Buyer is entitled to a return of all deposits, if any, less the appraisal fee and any other escrow expenses or fees chargeable to the Buyer. Thereafter, neither the Buyer, the Seller nor any brokers shall have any further rights, obligations, or liabilities under this contract.

APPRAISAL LOWER THAN SALES PRICE. All parties agree that it is possible that the property may not appraise for the full amount of the sales price. If the property does not appraise for the sales price, then the Buyer and Seller agree that the Buyer will increase the amount of down payment in order to close this transaction, provided that the additional amount of the down payment required under this paragraph shall not exceed $_____.

APPROVAL OF BUYER'S ACCOUNTANT. This offer is contingent upon the approval by Buyer's accountant of the terms of this offer within five (5) calendar days of acceptance; provided, however, that such approval will be deemed to be given unless written notice of disapproval is given within such time. If, for any reason, the Buyer's accountant disapproves of any of the terms of this offer, the Buyer may, at Buyer's option, declare this offer null and void and all deposits, if any, shall immediately be returned to the Buyer, less the amount of any escrow expenses or fees chargeable to the Buyer. Thereafter, neither the Buyer, the Seller nor any brokers shall have any further rights, obligations, or liabilities under this contract.

APPROVAL OF BUYER'S ATTORNEY. This offer is contingent upon the approval by Buyer's attorney of the terms of this offer within five (5) calendar days of acceptance; provided, however, that such approval will be deemed to be given unless written notice of disapproval is given within such time. If, for any reason, the Buyer's attorney disapproves of any of the terms of this offer, the Buyer may, at Buyer's option, declare this offer null and void and all deposits, if any, shall immediately be returned to the Buyer, less the amount of any settlement expenses or fees chargeable to the Buyer. Thereafter, neither the Buyer, the Seller nor any brokers shall have any further rights, obligations, or liabilities under this contract.

ASSIGNMENT OF SALES CONTRACT. Buyer may not assign or transfer this Sales Contract and/or Buyer's rights under this contract without the prior express written approval of the Seller. Seller agrees not to arbitrarily or unreasonably withhold consent. Buyer shall remain responsible for the performance of Buyer's obligations under the Sales Contract including payment of purchase price and timely closing.

BUILDING PERMITS. Seller agrees to provide permits for additions and/or renovations to the property which were not properly obtained or shown in the public records. Seller's cost to obtain permit(s), including costs to correct deficiencies required to obtain permits, shall not exceed $_____. If costs exceed this amount, Buyer and Seller shall, within five (5) calendar days from the determination of said costs, mutually agree in writing on the amount of the excess that each of the parties shall pay. If the parties fail to reach an agreement, this Sales Contract shall terminate, and all deposits shall be returned to Buyer less all settlement costs chargeable to Buyer.

BUILDING AND CONSTRUCTION WARRANTIES. Seller warrants that Seller used a licensed contractor and that this dwelling has been constructed in keeping with standards generally accepted in the community, that it is habitable, and that all elements, both interior and exterior, will be in a finished condition upon delivery. Seller shall convey to Buyer all existing contractor's guarantees: (a) against defective materials and workmanship and (b) that dwelling has been built in accordance with the plans and specifications. Should contractor's guarantees not exist or be insufficient to assure correction of defects within one year of recordation of this contract, Seller agrees to provide such warranty in accordance with this paragraph. Seller also warrants that (a) the design of the building is sufficient to avoid water penetration; (b) there are no mechanics liens on this property; and (c) that if time for filing liens has not expired and any mechanics liens due to Seller's responsibility are subsequently filed, Seller shall be financially responsible for clearing liens.

BUILDING PERMITS - BUYER. Buyer's obligations hereunder are contingent upon the Buyer obtaining a building permit to ___ (write in what permit is for) ___ within ____ (___) calendar days from acceptance of this offer. If Buyer is unable to obtain said permit within the time specified, Buyer shall have the right to terminate this contract by giving written notice to Seller; in such event, all deposits shall be returned to Buyer, less any escrow expenses chargeable to Buyer.

BUILDING PERMITS IN PLACE. Seller certifies that all the necessary building permits for the property improvements are in place, and that any required City and County inspections have been satisfactorily completed. If the necessary permits and approvals are not in place, Seller agrees at its expense to obtain said items. The Seller's cost to correct any and all non conformities shall not exceed $_____. If the value of repairs exceed this amount, Buyer and Seller shall mutually agree on how the additional cost shall be absorbed. If no agreement can be reached, this contract is null and void and all deposits shall be returned to Buyer, less escrow expenses chargeable to Buyer.

BUILDING PERMITS, LACK OF. Buyer is aware that the _____ _____ was built without a building permit, does not conform to the tax office records, and may not meet current building codes. Therefore, if the structure is destroyed in the future, Buyer may not be able to rebuild it under the present zoning code. In addition, Buyer is aware that to obtain a permit, the County Building Department may require additional work to be done and/or demolition of the existing improvements. The Seller shall not be required to make any repairs or pay for any expenses with respect to any nonconformance. The Buyer hereby accepts the property in this "as is" condition and releases and agrees to hold harmless, the Seller and the Seller's and Buyer's agents from any and all claims arising from or connected with said nonconformance and lack of building permits.

COMMON WALL & ENCROACHMENTS

ACCEPTANCE OF ENCROACHMENT. Buyer accepts the encroachment in its present "as is" and "where is" condition. Seller will not be required to correct or remove the encroachment. Buyer further releases Seller and ABC BROKER from any and all liability and claims related to the encroachment.

CORRECTION OF ENCROACHMENT. Seller, at Seller's sole expense, agrees to correct the encroachment prior to closing. The correction must be by way of removal of the encroachment or obtaining and recording an agreement which permits the encroachment to remain and grants the right to go upon the property being encroached upon to maintain the encroachment. Buyer's obligations under this contract are contingent upon Buyer's approval of such correction.

IF AGREEMENT IS AVAILABLE. The property is subject to a Common Wall Agreement with the adjacent property owner, and a copy of that agreement is attached. Buyer is advised to consult with legal counsel and/or other experts with respect to consequences of this agreement, and shall have seven (7) calendar days from the effective date of this contract to terminate this contract by giving written notice to

Seller or escrow if Buyer is not willing to accept the property with this agreement. If the Agreement is not recorded, Buyer and Seller agree to cooperate between themselves and the other parties to the Common Wall Agreement and to have it recorded at closing.

IF AGREEMENT IS NOT AVAILABLE; FAVORS BUYER. The property being conveyed has a common wall, portions of which are located on the subject property and an adjacent property. This offer is contingent upon the Seller, at Seller's cost and expense, within _____ (___) calendar days from the date of acceptance of this offer, 1) having the property staked and surveyed by a licensed surveyor, 2) providing Buyer with a location map by the surveyor showing the easement and properties involved, and 3) obtaining a Common Wall Agreement with the property owner who shares the common wall. Buyer is advised to consult with legal counsel and/or other experts with respect to consequences of this condition, and shall have seven (7) calendar days from the date of acceptance of this offer to terminate this contract by giving written disapproval to Seller or escrow if Buyer is not willing to accept this condition or the Seller cannot obtain a Common Wall Agreement. Buyer and Seller agree that the Agreement will be recorded.

IF AGREEMENT IS NOT AVAILABLE; FAVORS SELLER. The Buyer is aware that there is a "common wall" between this property and the adjoining property and that portions of this wall may be located on both properties. There is no written agreement between the affected properties regarding this condition. The wall was constructed at this location approximately _____ (___) years ago. Seller agrees to have the property staked by a licensed surveyor and to provide a location map showing the location of the wall and the properties involved by   (date) . Buyer is advised to consult with legal counsel and/or other experts with respect to consequences of this condition, and shall have seven (7) calendar days from completion of the survey and receipt of the location map to declare this contract null and void because of this condition by giving written disapproval to Seller or escrow. If no written disapproval is received within the time specified, Buyer accepts the "common wall" in its "as is" condition and at its present location and agrees to assume the responsibility for it.

CANCELLATION (BUYER). In the event cancellation occurs because Buyer is not able to perform, Buyer shall pay for all costs of cancellation, including costs of attorneys' fees, and other costs to cancel escrow and terminate this agreement. In addition, Buyer may be held to be in default under C-28 of the contract

CANCELLATION (SELLER). In the event cancellation occurs because Seller is not able to perform, Seller shall pay for all costs of cancellation, including costs of attorneys' fees, and other costs to cancel escrow and terminate agreement. In addition, Seller may be held to be in default under C-29 of the contract.

CONTINGENT ON ABILITY OF BUYER TO SELL PRESENT HOME. This offer is contingent on the ability of Buyer to sell Buyer's present property, located at _____   _____ ("Buyer's Home"), which Buyer shall diligently seek to sell expeditiously and in good faith, time being of the essence. Settlement on this contract will take place on or about the same time that settlement is conducted on the sale of the property of Buyer. It is agreed that if Seller receives a backup contract to this offer, Seller shall so notify the Buyer. Buyer will have _____ (___) hours following receipt of written notification from Seller or Seller's agent of the backup contract in which to remove this condition as well as any other contingency still unfulfilled which are contained in the offer made by Buyer or any contingencies or addenda attached and/or made a part thereto. If Buyer fails to remove the contingencies, then this contract shall be null and void and the deposit of Buyer shall be refunded in full; provided, however, that should the sale and closing of the Buyer' Home not be accomplished by _____ M. (Time) on _____(Date), Seller may declare this contract null and void by written or oral notification in which event the deposit of Buyer shall be refunded in full.

CONTINGENT ON SELLER FINDING REPLACEMENT HOME. Seller's obligations to sell the property are contingent upon Seller purchasing and closing upon a replacement house, and this contract, may be cancelled by Seller unless Seller or Seller's agent gives written notification to Buyer or Buyer's agent that Seller has purchased under contract a new house. If Seller has not removed this Addendum by _____ M.(Time) on _____ (Date), then this contract shall be null and void, and the deposit of Buyer shall be returned in full.

COUNTEROFFERS.   Buyer understands that Seller is providing counteroffers, unsigned by Seller, to two potential buyers simultaneously. Thus, Seller may receive offers signed by separate buyers for Seller's acceptance. Buyer agrees that Seller is free to accept either, or none, of the offers, and that Seller shall not be bound to Buyer unless Seller returns to Buyer the Counteroffer made by the Buyer and accepted by Seller.   If Buyer wishes to submit a Counteroffer to Seller, Buyer must do so by _____.

COUNTEROFFER, MULTIPLE.   Seller is making a Counteroffer(s) to another prospective buyer(s) on terms which may or may not be the same as in this Counteroffer. Acceptance of this Counteroffer by Buyer shall not be binding unless and until it is subsequently re-signed by Seller in paragraph 7 below and returned to Buyer or Buyer's agent. Prior to the completion of all of these events, Buyer and Seller shall have no duties or obligations for the purchase or sale of the Property.

COUNTERPART DOCUMENTS. This document may be executed in counterparts, each of which when executed shall, irrespective of when it is signed and delivered, be deemed an original, and said counterparts together shall constitute one and the same instrument.   Any deadlines specified in the contract remain applicable.

DEPOSITS AND DOWN PAYMENT

BUYER DEPOSITS NOT TIMELY.   If Buyer's initial deposit and/or any additional deposits required under the contract are not received by escrow by the time period specified in the contract, Buyer will be considered in default, and Seller may exercise the Seller's remedies in the contract. Time is of the essence in the payment of these deposits.

CASH FUNDS. Buyer shall provide satisfactory evidence of the availability of purchase funds within five (5) days of acceptance. If the Buyer is unable to provide satisfactory evidence within that time frame, Seller may declare this contract null and void with all deposits to be returned to Buyer. Buyer's lender is authorized to verify with Seller's agent that Buyer has sufficient funds available to close this transaction.

DOWN PAYMENT. Seller understands and Buyer represents that availability of Buyer's funds to cover the down payment is not conditioned and said funds are not obtained from any source which could cause a delay in the closing date specified in the contract.

PURCHASE FUNDS. Seller has the option to declare this contract null and void, if any earnest money deposits are not made on time as required by the contract or if Buyer's earnest money check does not clear.

Buyer to provide satisfactory evidence of the availability of cash funds within five (5) calendar days of acceptance. If Buyer is unable to provide satisfactory evidence within that time frame, Seller has the option to declare this contract null and void.

RELEASE OF BUYER'S DEPOSITS TO SELLER PRIOR TO CLOSE OF ESCROW. Buyer hereby instructs escrow irrevocably and without condition, to disburse prior to closing the sum of $_____ to the order of (Name of recipient) on (date).

In consideration of escrow releasing this sum as herein provided, the Buyer and Seller hereby indemnify and hold harmless escrow from and against any and all losses, costs, expenses, fees and claims which may arise or be incurred as a result of escrow's compliance with these irrevocable instructions for the early release of funds.

FINANCING

ASSUMPTION INCLUDE IN SPECIAL TERMS. Buyer may cancel this contract and recover all deposits previously made if (a) the principal balance of the mortgage to be assumed is less than $_____, or (b) upon assuming the mortgage, the interest rate will be higher than ____% per annum or the monthly payments therein required exceeds $_____, or (c) the assumption fee required to be paid is more than $_____, or (d) the Seller's consent to the assumption is required and Seller refuses to consent.

BUYER TO PAY DISCOUNT POINTS (WITH LIMIT). FHA discount points shall be paid by the Buyer, provided, however, if the points required to be paid exceed $_____ (or ____%), Buyer shall have the right to cancel this contract, by giving written notice to Seller, unless Seller agrees in writing to pay the excess amount (points). In the event of cancellation, the deposits previously made by the Buyer are to be refunded, less escrow expenses chargeable to Buyer.

CONTINGENCY TO REVIEW AND APPROVE MORTGAGE TO BE ASSUMED. Within ____ (___) calendar days from acceptance of this contract, Seller agrees to deliver to Buyer a copy of the First Mortgage, including any amendments. Any and all costs in obtaining the said document shall be paid by Seller. This offer is contingent upon the Buyer's review and approval of the Mortgage and amendment, if any, within ____ (___) calendar days of receipt from Seller; provided, however, that such approval will be deemed to be given unless written notice of disapproval is given within such time. If written disapproval is given within such time, this contract shall be null and void and all deposits shall be returned to Buyer. In the event that Seller fails to provide the Mortgage and amendment(s), if any, within the time specified, Buyer may, at Buyer's sole option, declare this contract null and void by delivering written notice to Seller or escrow, and all deposits shall be returned to Buyer.

FHA/VA LOAN. The origination fee (1%) is to be paid by the _____. FHA/VA discount points shall NOT exceed ____ percent (___%) of loan. The discount point(s) to be paid as follows with no more than: ____ (___) point(s) by Buyer, ____ (___) point(s) by Seller. _____ (Buyer/Seller) share of points shall be paid first and balance, if any, paid by _____ (Buyer/Seller). VA funding fee of ____ percent (___%) to be paid by _____. If the discount point required to be paid exceed the limit set above, and if the obligated party is not willing to pay their share, the obligated party(ies) may terminate this contract.

Buyer shall request for the appraisal immediately upon the loan application. In the event the FHA/VA appraised value is less than the purchase price, the Buyer shall notify the Seller, in writing, of Buyer's decision to either cancel this contract or proceed with the consummation of the transaction, within ____ (___) hours of notification of the FHA/VA appraised value, by lender.

IF BUYER IS LOOKING FOR A SPECIFIC TYPE OF ARM. If the Buyer is unable to obtain an ARM with a rate adjustment cap per period of ____% and a maximum rate cap of ____% over the initial rate, Buyer shall have the right to cancel this contract and recover all deposits previously made by giving written notice thereof to Seller on or before _____.

SELLER TO PAY DISCOUNT POINTS (WITH LIMIT). FHA discount points shall be paid by the Seller, provided, however, if the points required to be paid exceed $_____ (or ____%), Seller shall have the right to cancel this contract, by giving written notice to Buyer, unless Buyer agrees in writing to pay the excess. In the event of cancellation, the deposits previously made by Buyer are to be refunded, less escrow expenses chargeable to Buyer.

FEDERAL EMERGENCY MANAGEMENT AGENCY. Buyer is hereby advised to consult the FEMA studies with a civil engineer as they relate to flood zones which may affect subject property and either limit development of said property or result in a dangerous situation. Broker is not trained in water run-off and makes no representations, guarantees or warranties regarding surface water and how it may affect the Property.

NON-CONFORMING STRUCTURE. The property is zoned (type of zoning) and is a lawful non-conforming structure. The buildings do not conform with the current zoning laws of the City though they are permitted because they were constructed when a different zoning was in effect. As a non-conforming structure, there are restrictions on the owner's right to rebuild if the improvements are destroyed or demolished. This may cause problems with respect to financing, re-construction, repair, use, property values and re-sale. The Buyer understands the consequences of this non-conformity and agrees to accept this condition "AS IS." Buyer has not relied upon any statement or representation by Seller or ABC Broker concerning such structure.

NON-CONFORMING USE. Buyer acknowledges that the property is considered a legal non-conforming use in the zoning category of surrounding property. Buyer is independently satisfied as to whether or not the intended use is grandfathered and understands all the legal possibilities, ramifications and requirements relative to the use of the property.

NOTICES. Notices, requests, or demands by either Seller or Buyer shall be in writing and shall be delivered personally or mailed via registered or certified mail, postage prepaid, addressed to Seller or Buyer at their respective addresses herein set forth, with copies to the real estate agents and escrow officer. If mailed pursuant to this paragraph, notice shall be deemed given when mailed.

NOTICES IN WRITING - LONG VERSION. All notices required or permitted hereunder to be given to the parties to the contract or to escrow shall be given in writing by personal delivery by facsimile, or by depositing the same in the United States mail, registered or certified, return receipt requested, and postage prepaid. In each event, they shall be addressed to the parties or their respective broker at the addresses and/or facsimile numbers, as the case may be, set forth in the contract or to such other address or facsimile number as either party shall provide to the other party hereto in the manner set forth in this paragraph for the giving of notice. Any written notice sent by registered or certified mail shall be deemed to have been received by the addressee as of the date it is mailed in accordance with the foregoing provisions.

NOTICES IN WRITING - SHORT VERSION. Notices, requests, or demands by either party shall be in writing or shall be given personally, sent by facsimile transmission, or by Registered or Certified Mail, return receipt requested, postage prepaid, addressed to Seller and Buyer at the mail or fax addresses set forth herein. Notice shall be deemed given, when properly transmitted or deposited in the mails.

OCCUPANCY

BUYER RESPONSIBLE FOR SELLER'S LOSS OF RENT. If Seller gives the standard 45-day notice to vacate to a month-to-month tenant and Seller is able to deliver possession of the property to Buyer by the original scheduled closing date in the contract but Buyer is unable to close by that date for any reason through no fault of the Seller, then Buyer shall compensate Seller through escrow $_____ per day from the 46th day until the transaction is closed.

EARLY OCCUPANCY. Buyer and Seller understand and agree that Buyer is permitted to occupy the property prior to the close of escrow provided Buyer executes an "early occupancy agreement," a form of which is attached hereto and made a part of this contract.

EARLY OCCUPANCY. Seller agrees to deliver possession of the property at closing unless otherwise specified below. If possession is delivered prior to closing, Buyer assumes all risk of loss to the property from date of possession, and shall be responsible for maintenance, at Buyer's expense, and shall be deemed to have accepted the property, real and personal, in an "as is" condition as of the time of taking possession, the right of inspection to be exercised prior to the time of taking possession. Buyer should verify that there is adequate hazard insurance coverage during the Buyer's possession.

LATE OCCUPANCY. Seller shall have the right to remain in possession of the property for a period not to exceed _____ (___) days. Seller shall inform Buyer of Seller's election to exercise this right no later than ten (10) days prior to closing. Should Seller elect to exercise this right, Buyer and Seller herein agree to execute a rental agreement to cover a period of _____ (___) days commencing from date of recordation at a rate equal to the per diem amount of Buyer's new mortgage payment.

OFFERS AND COUNTEROFFERS

BACKUP OFFER. This is a backup offer and is in first position behind a primary contract now in escrow. All time frames of this contract shall commence after written notification from Seller to Buyer that the primary contract now in escrow has been cancelled. Buyer may, at Buyer's sole discretion, withdraw this backup offer prior to being notified by the Seller, in writing, that the primary contract has been cancelled. For the purpose of this contract, acceptance will be defined as that date the Buyer has been notified that the primary contract has been cancelled.

BUYER HAS OFFER ON ANOTHER PROPERTY. Seller is aware that Buyer has made an offer on another property and the acceptance of this offer by Seller is subject to the cancellation by all parties of the prior offer within seventy-two (72) hours of Seller's acceptance. If the offer is not cancelled, this offer will be deemed null and void, and all deposits will be returned to Buyer less all escrow costs chargeable to Buyer. If the prior offer is cancelled, this offer will remain in full force and effect.

BUYER IN BACKUP POSITION. Buyer acknowledges that this offer is a backup offer and that Seller accepts this offer contingent upon the written cancellation of the existing contract between the Seller and (Buyer's name), dated _____, no later than _____.

BUYER IN BACKUP POSITION -2. Buyer understands that this offer is a backup offer and there is an accepted primary contract on this property with the following contingencies: _____ _____. Buyer may cancel this contract at any time prior to receiving Seller's written notice that the primary contract has been cancelled and that this contract is in force.

SELLER TO TAKE BACKUP OFFERS AND REMOVAL CLAUSE. Seller may continue efforts to sell the subject property. If a third party submits an offer to purchase the property at a price and upon terms acceptable to Seller, Seller shall give written notice thereto to Buyer, and Buyer shall have _____ hours after receipt of the notice to amend this contract . If Buyer fails to execute and deliver such amendment in the time specified, Seller may accept the third party's offer, in which event, this contract shall be null and void, and Seller and Buyer shall be released from their obligations hereunder. All parties understand that time frames tagged to the "Date of Acceptance/Acknowledgement of this Offer" are amended to the date the Buyer notifies the Seller in writing that Buyer has accepted an offer on the Buyer's property.

SELLER WANTS TO TAKE BACKUP OFFERS. Seller reserves the right to continue marketing the property and to take secondary backup offers which would become a primary offer only in the event of Buyer's default or nonperformance of this contract. Buyer understands that the standard term of the contract covering Buyer defaults remains applicable even if the "backup" offer becomes the primary offer.

SIMULTANEOUS COUNTEROFFERS BY SELLER

A. Buyer understands that Seller has made a counteroffer from Seller to another buyer to sell the subject property. Until such time Seller notifies Buyer that the pending counteroffer has expired, or has been revoked by Seller, this counteroffer, if accepted by Buyer, constitutes a back up contract only.

B. Buyer is aware Seller is simultaneously making two counteroffers. In the event both counteroffers are accepted, then Seller reserves the right to choose one offer as the primary contract and to choose the second offer as a back-up position. Seller shall notify Buyers of their positions within two (2) days of receipt of the counteroffer's acceptance.

SIMULTANEOUS OFFERS BY BUYER. Seller understands that Buyer has made an outstanding offer on another property which is pending. If Seller decides to accept this contract, Seller agrees that within twenty-four (24) hours from the time Buyer receives a copy of the accepted offer, Buyer may either revoke any other pending offers which Buyer currently has made or may cancel this contract. If Buyer decides to cancel this contract, Buyer shall give Seller written notice by hand delivery or fax of Buyer's decision to cancel within twenty-four (24) hours, and Buyer shall be entitled to a refund of all deposits made in conjunction with this contract. Therefore, this contract will be void and neither Seller nor Buyer shall have any further responsibilities or obligations to each other under this contract.

OLDER HOME. Buyer understands that the subject property is not a new home but is approximately ____ (___) years old. Therefore, although Seller is not aware of any problem, it may not conform to current building codes. Buyer is strongly urged to (1) have a professional contractor or architect verify compliance with the building code and permit requirements, and (2) have a professional home inspection to ascertain the exact condition of the property.

PENDING CHANGES. Seller certifies that Seller knows of no easements, imminent or pending assessments, liens or lawsuits, upon or affecting said property and/or any association (if applicable) except as noted in the Seller's Disclosure Statement.

PENDING LEGAL ACTION. Buyer is aware and understands that the property is subject to the following current legal action: _____. Buyer is granted permission to contact the attorney and the Association regarding the legal action.

PERSONAL PROPERTY

BILL OF SALE. Buyer and Seller understand and agree that the personal property described in the attached inventory is not included in the sales price and will be transferred to Buyer by way of a Bill of Sale to be paid through escrow at closing for a total purchase price of $_____.

BLUEPRINTS. Seller agrees to deliver to Buyer prior to closing all blueprints, architect's drawings, landscape architect designs, and all building and landscaping specifications, surveys and maps describing the property, presently in the Seller's possession.

FAVORS BUYER. Seller shall provide Buyer with a complete inventory of all items to be included in the sale of this property within five (5) calendar days of acceptance of this offer. Buyer shall approve same in writing within three (3) calendar days of receipt or this offer shall be null and void with all deposits returned to Buyer less any escrow expenses chargeable to Buyer.

FAVORS SELLER. The purchase price includes those items on the inventory list attached hereto. These items are being conveyed in "AS IS" condition. This offer is contingent upon the Buyer's examination and approval of the inventory within five (5) calendar days from acceptance of this offer. If Buyer does not approve of inventory, Buyer may declare this contract null and void by giving written notice to Seller within the time specified. No response from the Buyer within the time specified shall be deemed approval.

INVENTORY. Seller to provide Buyer with a complete furniture inventory within five (5) calendar days of acceptance of this offer. Buyer's obligation to buy is conditioned upon Buyer's written approval of same within three (3) calendar days of receipt.

PERSONAL PROPERTY. The personal property and fixtures listed in this contract are included in the purchase price and shall be the same property shown to Buyer or located in the property immediately prior to the signing of this contract. Seller or Seller's agents shall make no substitutions unless agreed to by Buyer in a written agreement signed by both Buyer and Seller.

PRIVATE ROAD. Buyer is hereby advised that subject property is located on a private road which may require that Buyer contribute to the maintenance of said road for continued access. Buyer should have his attorney review the roadway agreement (if one exists) and advise Buyer accordingly. Some lending sources may refuse to provide financing if no maintenance agreement exists or is insufficient in form.

PROFESSIONAL'S DISCLAIMER. Buyer is aware that (name of Seller) is a licensed (contractor, architect, etc.) . Buyer acknowledges that Seller has made no representations as a (contractor, architect, etc.) to Buyer. Buyer is advised to, and has a right to, use professionals of Buyer's choice to inspect the property under the contract.

PROPERTY CONDITION

AS IS. The Buyer is given every opportunity to inspect the property and is aware of the following conditions: _____

_____

_____

_____

as well as all of the conditions disclosed in the attached Seller's Real Property Disclosure Statement dated _____, which disclosures are incorporated herein by reference. With full knowledge of these conditions, the Buyer is aware, understands and agrees that all land, improvements and real and personal property will be sold, conveyed and/or assigned, as applicable, by the Seller to the Buyer in an "AS IS" condition without warranty or representation, express or implied, the Buyer hereby agreeing, acknowledging and affirming to the Seller that the Buyer has had full opportunity to inspect, and accepts all land, improvements and real and personal property in an "AS IS" condition, including the conditions disclosed above. Buyer understands and acknowledges that the Seller hereby expressly disclaims any and all warranties, whether express or implied, with respect to the land, improvements, and real and personal property, including without limitation, any warranty of habitability, warranty of merchantability, or warranty of fitness for a particular use. It is the Buyer's intention to give up, waive, and relinquish all rights to assert any claim, demand, or lawsuit of any kind with respect to the condition of the land, the improvements, the real property, or the personal property. The Seller will not be required to make any repairs or pay any expenses concerning the land, the improvements, the real property, or the personal property.

IF REPAIRS ARE NOT EXPECTED TO BE COMPLETED BY CLOSING. It is mutually agreed that in the event repairs cannot be completed by closing, escrow shall withhold from Seller's proceeds the estimated cost of repairs agreed to by Seller. Repair bills shall be paid through escrow, and any balance remaining undisbursed shall be returned to Seller upon completion of repairs. Seller's agent shall send list of repairs to be done and estimated costs to escrow prior to closing.

SOILS CONDITION - EXAMPLE OF DISCLOSURE. Buyer is aware that the soils condition of the property is unstable. The retaining wall on the rear side of the property shows cracks which may be due to settlement. The Buyer accepts the property in "AS IS" condition with respect to such soils condition and settlement and the possible consequences of this condition. The Seller makes no warranty of any kind with respect thereto.

SOILS INSPECTION CONTINGENCY. Within seven (7) calendar days of acceptance of this contract, Buyer may, at Buyer's expense, have a soils inspection conducted by experts/representatives of Buyer's choice. This offer is contingent upon Buyer's approval of the soils reports within five (5) calendar days from the date of inspection; provided, however, that such approval shall be deemed to be given unless written notice of disapproval is given within such time. Seller shall give reasonable access to the property to Buyer and/or representatives.

PROPERTY DISCLOSURE

ASBESTOS - SELLER. Seller suspects, or knows about, the existence of asbestos on the property. Seller makes no warranty or representation about the nature or condition of such asbestos. Seller makes no representation as to whether this material must be removed, repaired or maintained in any way, pursuant to state and/or federal environmental laws. Buyer is encouraged to retain experts to obtain appropriate advice.

ASBESTOS - BUYER. Seller represents that asbestos or hazardous substance exists on or under the property. Seller agrees to defend and indemnify Buyer and hold Buyer harmless from and against any claim, demand, liability, damages, penalties, costs or expenses (including attorney's fees) arising from the existence of any hazardous substance or waste on the subject property, or from any action on account thereof taken by governmental authorities under either state or federal environmental laws. This includes, but is not limited to, all costs incurred in removing and disposing the hazardous material in the manner permitted by law.

ACCESS (LEGAL). Seller warrants that there is legal access between the property and a public roadway. If property does not border a public street, road or highway, Seller shall, on or before fifteen (15) days prior to closing, furnish to Buyer, at Seller's expense, one of the following: (1) copy of a recorded access easement, running in favor of any and all title holders of the property; or (2) an easement in recordable form, from the (servient) owners of the property over which the easement is to run, and running in favor of Buyer, Buyer's heirs, assigns, and successors in title. Seller shall pay for recording said easement and all other related expenses.

ASSESSMENTS. The Seller represents that as of _____, there are no past due, current, or known future assessments affecting the subject property except as follows: _____ _____. If, (1) as of the date of this agreement, there are any past due, current, or known future assessments affecting the subject property which have not been disclosed by Seller, or (2) any assessments are authorized or become known prior to the closing date of this contract, then Buyer reserves the right to declare this contract null and void and recover all deposits unless either (a) the assessments which are owed at or before closing are paid in full by Seller prior to closing, or (b) the assessments known to be due after closing will be paid in full by Seller from funds left in escrow for that purpose. If Seller obtains any information prior to closing concerning assessments not disclosed herein, that information shall promptly be disclosed to Buyer in writing.

CATCHMENT WATER. The Buyer understands: that water service to this property is by catchment system only; that lead contamination or other problems can occur with this type of water system; that the quantity of water from this system may be insufficient at times and the water may need to be obtained from other sources. Buyer accepts the property with its existing catchment water system subject to these risks and agrees not to assert any claims against the Seller and the Seller's agents.

CESSPOOL. Buyer is aware that the property is not connected to the sewer and that a cesspool is currently used for sewage disposal. An additional cesspool or septic tank system must be built to accommodate an additional structure if allowed, and appropriate permits and minimum lot size may be required before a second cesspool or septic tank system will be permitted. Buyer has received, reviewed, and been advised to contact the State Department of Health regarding current cesspool policy. Buyer is further aware that this policy may change at any time, and Buyer is accepting the property without any representation, statements or promises by Seller or ABC broker regarding cesspools.

COMMUNITY ASSOCIATION DUES. Buyer is aware that the property is located in an area or neighborhood which assesses fees for _____. These fees are currently $_____ per _____ and may increase in the future.

DISCLAIMER RE BUILDING ORDINANCES. Buyer acknowledges that Buyer has investigated the local governmental zoning and building ordinances and requirements as to the erection of a building on the property, and that Buyer has investigated the availability of water, sewer, gas, and electrical services for the property, and the fees and costs related thereto. Buyer further acknowledges that Buyer is relying solely upon data obtained by Buyer from outside sources on all these matters and is not relying upon any representations made by Seller or its agents.

DISCLOSURE STATEMENT. This offer is contingent upon the approval by Buyer of the Seller's Disclosure Statement within _____ (___) days of receipt from Seller. If Buyer fails to provide written notice of approval within the prescribed time, this offer shall be considered terminated and the Termination Provision shall apply.

HOMEOWNER'S INSURANCE. Buyer is hereby advised that it may be necessary to purchase additional WIND/HURRICANE coverage in order to obtain a loan secured on the property from any federally regulated financial institution or guaranteed by an agency of the U.S. Government. Buyer is advised to consult with an insurance company of Buyer's choice to determine the cost and availability of the additional WIND/HURRICANE coverage in Buyer's Homeowner's Insurance Policy. Buyer is also aware that a Homeowners' Insurance Policy may not be available at this time and that this condition is beyond the Seller's control or responsibility. Buyer understands and agrees that this offer is NOT contingent upon Buyer's ability to obtain such an insurance policy.

RENTAL POOLS. Buyer understands that this apartment in the project known as _____ is being sold in an isolated resale transaction, that neither Seller nor ABC Broker is the developer of said project, nor an affiliate thereof, nor the manager of the management entity nor an affiliate thereof. Buyer further affirms that the entire consideration paid in this transaction pertains to and is applicable to the condominium apartment and appurtenant interests in the common elements of said project (i.e., real property) and that no separate consideration has been paid or will be paid for the interest, if any, in the rental management entity, transferred with said apartment. Buyer also understands that the Seller and its agents are not offering directly or indirectly a rental service of any kind to the owners of condominium apartment units in the project, either individually or in any form of pooling arrangement, or by a third party designated or arranged for by Seller, nor have any representations been made by the Seller or its agents as to the feasibility of renting the apartment or otherwise generating income or deriving any other economic benefit from ownership of the apartment.

REMOVAL CLAUSE. Seller reserves the right to continue marketing the Property and to accept back-up offers. Buyer agrees that if the Seller accepts one or more back-up offers, the Buyer shall have 72 hours, after written notice to the Buyers, to waive and remove [all contingencies] [the following numbered contingencies: _____] by way of a written waiver of contingency delivered to Escrow. If the contingency is not waived and removed as required by this paragraph, then this offer shall be null and void.

RETURN OF ALL SELLER'S DOCUMENTS. In the event the transaction does not close, the Buyer agrees to return to the Seller all documents and disclosures that Buyer has received within SEVEN (7) days of Buyer's signing of a cancellation notice. Failure to do so before the Seller signs the cancellation notice will result in escrow being instructed to withhold $50.00 from the Buyer's deposit and deliver it to the Seller to cover Seller's costs to replace lost documents and disclosures.

RIGHT OF FIRST REFUSAL. If, during the term of the lease, or any extension thereof, Lessor shall receive an offer to purchase this property or if Lessor shall wish to enter into an agreement for the sale of this property, Lessor shall first give Lessee written notice setting forth the name of the proposed purchaser, the purchase price, and all the terms and conditions of the proposed sale. Within ___ (___) calendar days following the delivery or mailing of said notice pursuant to the terms of this lease, Tenant shall have the right to purchase the property upon the same terms and conditions. Said right shall be exercised by delivering or mailing such election to Owner prior to the expiration of said calendar days. If Tenant shall not elect to make such purchase within said time, and the sale is made in accordance with the terms set forth in the notice, Tenant shall not have a right to purchase upon any resale.

RISK OF LOSS. If the improvements are damaged by fire or other casualty prior to closing, and the cost of restoration does not exceed five percent of the assessed valuation of the improvements damaged, the Seller shall restore the improvements at Seller's expense, and the time for closing shall be extended sixty (60) days. If the cost of restoration exceeds five percent of the assessed valuation of the improvements damaged, the Buyer shall have the option of taking the property "as is," together with any insurance proceeds payable by virtue of such damage, or canceling this contract and receiving a refund of all deposits made hereunder. Seller shall maintain standard hazard and extended perils coverage of casualty insurance with a reputable company until time of closing, but shall not be required to restore if cost of restoration will exceed five percent of the assessed valuation of the improvements damaged.

SELLER'S PRIOR CONTRACT. Buyer is aware that Seller has an accepted "primary contract" on subject property and that this offer is a backup offer that will be placed in first position if the current "primary contract" is cancelled for any reason. Seller agrees to inform Buyer in writing within _____ (___) days from when the current "primary contract" is consummated or cancelled, whichever is the case. If the primary contract is cancelled, Seller shall provide evidence of formal cancellation.

Buyer has the unilateral right to cancel this contract at any time prior to receiving written notice from Seller that this offer has become the primary contract. Buyer may cancel by giving timely written notice to Seller or escrow.

SPECIFIC REPAIRS TO BE DONE BY SELLER. 1) Leaking Roof to be Repaired: The Buyer is aware that the family room roof leaks. The Seller, at Seller's sole cost and expense, agrees to have the roof above the family room repaired by a licensed roofing contractor prior to closing. However, Seller does not warrant that it will not leak in the future and makes no representations in this regard. 2) Ice-maker to be Repaired or Replaced: Buyer is aware that the ice-maker does not work. The Seller, at Seller's sole cost and expense, agrees to have the ice-maker professionally repaired or replaced with one of similar type prior to closing.

TAX EXCHANGE. If the Property qualifies for exchange treatment, both Seller and Buyer reserve the right to restructure this transaction as an exchange (including, but not limited to, a tax deferred exchange under Section 1031 of the Internal Revenue Code of 1986 as amended), provided that such restructuring does not delay the closing of this transaction in any way and does not result in the imposition of any additional costs or liabilities upon the other party, and provided further that exchange treatment is not a contingency to this contract.

TAX AND EXCHANGE

FIRPTA. Seller agrees to comply with federal (FIRPTA) and state tax withholding laws. Escrow is hereby notified, and Seller agrees and irrevocably instructs and authorizes escrow to withhold all necessary funds for compliance unless Seller provides escrow prior to closing with appropriate waivers or exemptions.

WHEN BUYER WANTS A 1031 EXCHANGE. Seller is informed that Buyer intends to include the property as a replacement property in a Section 1031 exchange of properties. Seller agrees to cooperate in effecting said exchange by signing all necessary and appropriate exchange documents. Buyer agrees to indemnify and hold Seller harmless from all costs, expenses and liabilities incurred by Seller because of Buyer's participation in said exchange. Seller is not required to assume temporary ownership of any other property. ABC Broker and its sales agents are not responsible for any value set by the principals to the exchange. ABC Broker advises principals to seek competent legal and tax counseling regarding IRC Section 1031 Exchange. Principals are not relying on any representations in this regard by ABC Broker or its sales agents.

WHEN SELLER WANTS A 1031 EXCHANGE. Buyer is informed that Seller intends to include the property as a relinquished property in a Section 1031 exchange. Buyer agrees to cooperate in effecting said exchange by signing all necessary and appropriate exchange documents. Seller agrees to indemnify and hold Buyer harmless from all costs, expenses, and liabilities incurred by Buyer because of Seller's participation in said exchange. Buyer is not required to assume temporary ownership of other property. ABC Broker and its sales agents are not responsible for any value set by the principals to the exchange. ABC Broker advises principals to seek competent legal and tax counseling regarding IRC Section 1031 Exchange. Principals are not relying on any representations by ABC Broker or its agents.

TERMITE. Buyer understands that even though the referenced provisions require the Seller to disclose any prior and/or current infestation or damage that the Seller is aware of, Seller and Buyer are lay persons with no expertise in detecting termite damage, and therefore may not be aware of, or fully or accurately describe, any existing problems.

TERMITE DAMAGE. If the termite inspection reveals any damage, Seller shall pay for the costs to repair such damage, including the cost of repairing or replacing the affected improvements, except that such cost to Seller shall not exceed $_____. Repairs shall include correcting any structural damage which may be required by the lender to be repaired or restored prior to closing.

If the cost of repair exceeds this amount, and the Buyer does not agree to pay for the excess amount, then Seller shall have the option to cancel the contract by giving written notice to Buyer within ___ (___) calendar days of receipt of the termite report and the estimated cost of such repairs or replacement.

TERMITE INSPECTION CONTINGENCY.   (Buyer or Seller)   shall be responsible for up to but no more than $_____ toward the cost of said termite inspection. If Seller selects the licensed pest control company, Seller shall be responsible for the total cost of said inspection.

TITLE INSURANCE; RESPA RULE RE BUYER'S TITLE INSURANCE CHOICE.   Buyer understands that Seller will be obtaining the title report from (Name of Title Co.) and since it is less expensive to obtain the mortgagee's title policy from the same title company, Buyer authorizes and directs (Name of Escrow Co.) to obtain the mortgagee's title policy from the same company at a cost of $_____, which Buyer agrees to pay at time of closing.

VACANT LAND. This offer is subject to the Buyer's approval of the restrictive covenants, locations and evidence of utilities available and actual hook-up of these utilities, and _____. Seller shall deliver these items to Buyer within five (5) calendar days of acceptance of this offer. Buyer may declare this contract null and void and recover all deposits if Buyer does not approve of the items; provided, however, that approval will be deemed to be given if written disapproval is not delivered to Seller within five (5) calendar days of receipt of items.

Part III:
ADVANCED STRATEGIES

Exercise #22
Going to "Contracts"

Once your offer is accepted, you go into something called "contracts." Your original LOI or offer is not recorded anywhere. It's not something that a lender will see. If you indicated anything about seller financing, this is not a document that you have to worry about being "official" on any level. The contracts are usually drawn up by the seller's listing agent or attorney. This is a good time to have these contracts either be reviewed thoroughly by your (buyer's) agent or an attorney. This is *not* a good time to play the attorney role and assume that you will understand all of the legalese in the contract otherwise you are *probably* going to end up losing your ass in the process.

The contract portion is what identifies the legal aspects of the deal including the legal property description (APN, number of acres, building square footage, etc.), contingency periods, deposit amounts (and due dates), dates of closing, penalty periods, amounts of money that will be lost if the contract periods or terms are violated, etc. A typical contract will run anywhere from 5 to 10 pages and you could easily be blinded with the heavy legal language that is used. This is why a real estate attorney is instrumental in successfully navigating this paperwork.

By the way, make sure that you have a real estate attorney come into the process at this point (and not a moment earlier). You don't merely want a business contract attorney. You want an attorney licensed in the state of the property deal who has extensive real estate contract knowledge. Since real estate contracts is a small facet of the law, many real estate attorneys do not exclusively practice real estate law but rather have a listing of other law they routinely practice; you will usually not be successful in finding an attorney that exclusively practices real estate law so don't get frustrated when you can't find one.

Ask if they have experience with commercial real estate. Commercial and residential real estate have much different contingency periods, inspection requirements, and other differences. This is why commercial real estate needs to be something the attorney has experience with.

You may not have reached this phase but you need to do this assignment anyway. Do an online search to find "commercial real estate attorneys" in the state of the property deal. You want to have a short list before you will need to pick up the phone to call these people. You don't want to be scrambling around for an attorney *after* the contracts have been given to you.

Please work through these questions:

1) Do some Internet research for commercial real estate attorneys in your property farming area. How many were you able to locate? Write down their names, areas of specialty, and contact information below:

2) Call a couple of them on the phone just to get a feel for their personality. Find out if they have experience with commercial real estate transactions. Explain that you are about to go to contracts on a property deal and you will need them to review a draft contract. Ask what their rates are and indicate your responses below:

3) If you find that you are doing many deals per month, consider getting on a monthly legal plan. It's like an insurance policy except much cheaper. For more information, visit **www.RealEstateLegalPlans.com**. This allows you access to attorneys of every specialty nationwide. If you are looking at deals in multiple states, this gives you an advantage to find someone specialized (and fast) without paying an arm and a leg. Many times attorneys will charge $250 to $750 (minimum) to go through a draft contract. If you are doing this monthly, this gets expensive. A legal plan is less than $100 per month but is something you should only look at doing when you become a serious investor doing many deals per year. Take a look at the website above but, again, don't sign up until later. Record the information you've been able to extract below for later use including types of plans and monthly cost:

Exercise #23
Due Diligence

After your contracts are signed off by the seller then you are now going into escrow. If you have an earnest money deposit, it will be collected at this time and used as the opening deposit for the escrow account. If you do not have an earnest money deposit (and hopefully you weren't foolish enough to offer one if you don't have it) then you can use $100 to open the escrow account at this time.

In the due diligence process, you will be getting the official numbers and rundown on everything. Hopefully when you asked for "actual" income and expenses earlier, the listing agent or seller gave you real numbers instead of phony numbers. If they lied about the income/expenses, occupancy level, etc. then this is the time when you will discover these lies. If you weren't aggressive in the beginning (or during contracts) to demand 3 years of actual income and expenses then this is when they legally have to furnish this documentation…otherwise you can back out of the deal with no financial or legal recourse.

You'll notice in bad economic times that much of what a listing agent or seller will tell you is nothing but a boatload of lies in an effort to sell their property. What many of these people don't understand is that conventional lenders will need to *verify* all income/expense documentation including verifiable occupancy levels otherwise they will *not* fund the property deal. Some sellers (and listing agents, believe it or not) still think we are functioning under the "old school" system where you could simply bamboozle a lender (and buyer) into believing that their verbal (and physically manipulated profit/loss) statements about the performance of a property will suffice in closing the deal. Fortunately (for you), this doesn't work anymore under today's lending rules but many of the lying fools you'll deal with still don't know this.

Part of the due diligence process includes your lender or bank ordering the appraisal. You *never* order your own appraisal as you may for a residential property deal. Let the bank or lender order the appraisal otherwise, chances are, they won't accept the appraiser you chose so, $4,000 later, you'll realize that the bank will *not* accept the appraisal report and will have to order a new appraisal anyway. And no, an appraisal done by the seller up to 6 months ago will *not* be acceptable to the lender so don't try to offer it up as a substitution for a new ordered appraisal. This ploy will *not* work.

This is why it's *critical* that you do the due diligence by getting the official "numbers" *before* the bank orders the appraisal. You create a contingency period in your offer and contracts that make the seller provide all verifiable paperwork within 14 days of the date that you enter into escrow. Make sure you pound on them to provide this paperwork so the bank doesn't order the appraisal until *after* you can see their financials. If they are late on providing the paperwork, then terminate the deal immediately. Make this very clear from the moment the process starts so that if they believe they will be pulling some shenanigans with delay, B.S., and foot-dragging, you won't be closing and they won't be selling. It's as simple as that.

What are the official documents? This would include the last 3 years of tax returns that the owner filed on behalf of the property, usually on behalf of the LLC. This should breakdown the performance of the property including the reported income, expenses, and property taxes. You need the last 3 years. If the statements show that they are paying much more in expenses than they initially indicated to you then you need to tell them that these numbers do not support what they said before. Many times they will say, "Well, I just told the IRS that I pay my landscaper $10,000 a year when really I pay the guy $5,000 a year." And they will systematically say this for every expense reported. That's when you need to tell them, "Listen, I have to base my future cash flow projections on verifiable numbers. If you lied to the IRS, that's your business. I can only go on what you said here. We need to drop the asking price and do an addendum on the final purchase price otherwise I'm pulling out of this deal."

If they argue, simply tell them that you will get someone on the phone with the IRS and perhaps they wish to explain to "Mr. Jones" with the Department of Treasury that they lied on their tax return; this is how you wish to handle the transaction at this point. Usually this will shut them up really fast!

Other due diligence items you will need: recent bank statements going back monthly for the past 12 months. This will allow you to see what the Gross Operating Income (GOI) is that is being deposited monthly into the account. Look at the deposits. You will then get the past 12 rent rolls (which come out monthly) to check this information against the bank statements to see if it matches. You may see a 90% occupancy on the rent roll but the deposits show that only 70% of the tenants are paying rent and the others need to be evicted. This is a problem. This means that you will have to evict a pile of deadbeats (which is very expensive) if you are lucky to get the lender to fund the deal (because they will also be looking at the same documentation you are looking at).

You can have a CPA run an "audit" on the paperwork but this takes time (and money) and you may *not* have time if you are waiting on the appraisal to be ordered and then the building inspection shortly thereafter. So, you can either have a CPA lined up (and he can be local to you but 2,000 miles away from the property; he or she doesn't need to be in the state of the transaction) to quickly dive into the paperwork you have but if it's anywhere between January 15th through April 15th, forget about using a CPA otherwise you will be waiting a very long time to get a response. And time is of the essence.

Warning: If at *any* point in time the seller is dragging his feet on giving you the financial documentation on the property, this is *almost always* a sign that he *doesn't* have the paperwork to verify his expenses and/or income. This is when you drop out of the deal immediately before an appraisal and building inspection is done. Don't cry over spilled milk thinking that the seller needed "more time." He either has the paperwork or he doesn't; it should be as simple as running over to Kinko's to run off copies of his tax records, bank statements, and his QuickBooks profit/loss statement. If he doesn't have this basic financial documentation then he's lied all along about the performance of the property and you don't want the deal anyway. And if he has a song and dance about how he doesn't keep profit/loss spreadsheets, he's lying through his teeth. Everyone is *required by law* to keep financial records on any business (including a cash flow property which is a tax-reporting "business"), especially since everyone needs to file annual taxes. If they are claiming that the records don't exist then they are hiding details about the financial performance of the property. At this point you need to *run* from the property deal as quickly as possible.

Finally, after the financials check out and the bank sends out an appraiser, you need to order a building inspection. Many lenders are now requiring to see a building inspection report before they will lend on the deal to make sure there is a structurally sound building on the property. You can choose whichever building inspection company you want. Make sure they are "aged" in years and experience; you want the company that's been in business for 20 or more years. You also want to find a company that will be paid out of escrow through escrow instructions, especially if the seller is not paying for these due diligence costs through the "seller concession" that you should have demanded when you submitted your initial LOI/offer.

Work through these exercises:

1) Based on the reading in this section, make a listing of all the "due diligence" including the financial documentation you will have to line up during the escrow phase. Don't forget about the bank-ordered appraisal or building inspection. Include a comprehensive listing of the financial documentation you will need to see and add some extra details that you can think of that maybe I didn't include above. (i.e. "Certified/notarized CPA signature on CPA letterhead to verify the accuracy of all claims, etc." Do *not* use such a document, however, in place of actual filed IRS statements, real bank statements, etc. You can use such a document *in addition to* the other official financial documentation and *not* in lieu of.)

2) Do some research on CPAs that specialize in real estate transactions or who do the "books" for commercial cash flow properties. This CPA can be someone you know (just check to see if they handle commercial real estate) or someone you do research on who is local to you (even if the property deals are out of state). Write down a short list of 3 – 5 CPAs you have been able to locate who can handle your future needs in this department. You may have to call them to be sure they can handle a *financial audit* on a commercial real estate deal.

3) Do some research that is local to your property farm area on building inspectors in the area. You want ones that specialize in residential-commercial and/or commercial property inspections (and not just residential). Make note of their length of time in business. Call a few to get a feel for their personalities, if they really can inspect a commercial property (and what their experience is in this department), and how long it takes them to inspect an apartment building that is, say, 24 units. (By the way, an inspector will *not* be inspecting all of the units of the property. This will be too costly, time consuming, and will upset the current tenants. He will be inspecting a *cross-section* of about 10% to 20% of the units to get an idea of the age of the appliances, plumbing systems inside, etc. All of the other units will be the same provided that all of the buildings in the complex were built in the same year or thereabouts.) Make a list of at least 3 building inspectors that meet the basic criteria (which is in business for 20 years or longer and have a lot of experience inspecting residential-commercial properties).

Exercise #24
Creating a Management Plan

While in escrow, you will be doing quite a bit. You will have to make sure you audit the real financials that come in (or crack the whip on the CPA who needs to give you a full accountability report), making sure the appraiser comes in post-audit (instead of before) as ordered by the lender/bank, and then getting a qualified building inspector out to the property.

But that's not all. During this phase you need to start outlining a solid and streamlined management plan so that you can hit the ground running the second you close escrow. You don't want to be standing there with your HUD-1 statement, staring at your property, and scratching your head...wondering what to do next! You need to know *exactly* what you'll be doing the moment you close!

My methodology of management is much different than most other "gurus" out there. Everyone else seems to want to get a management company and step away from the full responsibility of their building. While this sounds really good, I can tell you from experience that you will get burned through a property management service, especially when it's clear that you are an out of state investor.

You can automate your management process, even for out of state properties, while remaining in maximum control. No, I don't recommend the "Ethel and Fred Mertz" style of management where the owners live on premises; the wife leases out units and collects rent while the husband does all the Band-Aid repair work. This will burn you out faster than you can say "cash flow."

Now it's time for you to sketch out a basic management plan. Here are my suggestions based on property unit size:

Amount of Units	Management	Maintenance Handled By...	Leasing Handled By...
5 – 20	No onsite or offsite	24/7 "on call" maintenance service	Residential real estate agent
21 – 50	"Live in" onsite manager	"Live in" onsite manager	"Live in" onsite manager or residential real estate agent
51 – 100	"Live in" onsite manager (husband/wife team preferred)	"Live in" onsite manager + 24/7 "on call" maintenance service	"Live in" onsite manager only
101+	Onsite management "office" on the property	Management service on the property with at least 1 dedicated maintenance employee	Onsite management office; usually the office manager or assistant manager

For apartment complexes over 100 units, your may considering staffing as follows:

Units	Manager	Assistant Manager	Administrative Staff	Maintenance Crew
101 – 150	1	0	1	1
151 – 200	1	1	0	2
201 – 250	1	1	1 - 2	2
250 – 300	1	1	2	3 - 4
301 – 400	1	2	2	4 - 5
401 – 500	1	2	3	5 - 6

Remember, when you have over 100 units in a single complex then you should seriously consider having a small "office" onsite to handle the business of the building. It can be as simple as using a small apartment unit to house the office or building a "modular" office space for your staff.

Your onsite management service will handle all of the internal workings of the business. They will be staffed by the property LLC. They will receive a regular paycheck, healthcare benefits, and you will have to furnish Worker's Comp insurance. Your manager will have access to the banking information. The office will receive rental payments, input them into a software computer system (Intuit's *Real Estate Solutions* software is recommended), deposit the funds and payout on all expenses. You can also have them pay on your mortgage (or you can do it yourself).

It is a requirement that you have your staff and all of the property financial activities closely monitored by yourself. They should submit monthly profit/loss reports to you. You should view the activity of the LLC bank account online at least twice weekly to see if there is unusual activity taking place.

The most important thing about using this set up is that you need to be sure to use a CPA to audit the books quarterly at these precise intervals: April (for the first quarter), July (for the second quarter), October (for the third quarter), and January (for the fourth quarter of the prior year). Do not drop the ball on the outside audit. Make sure you are consistent with having a CPA perform this important service for you to keep the property financials under control and to ensure that no one is mismanaging the property funds.

Please answer these questions:

1) On the property deals you are working on presently, which management strategies should you consider based on the information presented above?

2) Why is it probably not a good idea to get an outside management company involved, especially if you are an out-of-state property owner?

3) If you wish to consider an outside property management service, it's not out of the question. However, it's wise to do a lot of research on the service including getting referrals and interviewing these referrals personally. Consider using a very small firm and meet personally with the main manager to see if you have a rapport and "understanding" with him or her about how a property should be run. If you are out of state, consider flying in to meet with different managers to see if you can interview them in person. Based on my personal management methodology and given the information I just presented above about seeking out a management service for an out-of-state property, which methodology would you prefer to use for your properties? Please explain which method seems to be most suitable for you?

4) When you first take over a building that has tenancy problems that have to be "cured" right away or a property that needs extensive rehab, plan on being near or on the property until you can take control of the property before passing the reigns onto someone else. In this process, you will be actively looking for and interviewing managers (whether it's a management service or an onsite manager you will be putting in place), marketing your units or getting them fixed through contractors, and putting your property back into full functioning order. Since this will be necessary for many of your properties, do you find that doing this is something that you are willing to do…or not? If so, please indicate that you are willing to do what it takes to make your property successful. If you are not willing to do this, please indicate why.

Exercise #25
Your Exit Strategy

One of the most important things you will need to determine very early on is what your exit strategy is. Most people think an exit strategy means only one thing: what will I do with the property to "exit" the transaction at a later date? Will I buy and hold? Will I flip it? When will I be getting rid of it?

The true definition of "exit strategy" is two-fold. It really means what you will do with the property the moment you get your hands on it (i.e. rehab, cure vacancy problem with a specific plan, etc.) *and* what you plan on doing with it overall (buy and hold for 27.5 years, buy then rehab to flip it in 24 months, etc.) This is something you should have been thinking about long before you put in your initial offer. During the escrow process, you will be refining your exit strategy to make sure you have everything properly aligned with your overall investing goals.

Please work through these questions:

1) What is your overall investment strategy in how you want to handle most of your property acquisitions? Do you want to buy and hang onto them forever (as I recommend)? Do you want to buy, rehab, lease up the units and flip them within 2 years for a profit? Do you want to pick up "don't want" property deals with a lot of value-add potential because you are a contractor, for instance, and you can rehab your buildings cheaply? If so, do you plan on holding onto your properties or flipping them post-rehab? These are all questions you need to address at this stage which will help make it easier for you to locate the types of property deals you should be focusing on in the future.

2) Do you plan on picking up a lot of smaller buildings and perhaps manage them yourself if they are local to you? If not, what is your desired strategy?

Exercise #26
Understanding Advanced Terms

It's time to test some of your advanced knowledge so far. I want to make sure you understand some of the basic terminology that has been introduced in *Apartment Building Millionaire* from Chapter 5 through Chapter 10.

1) Which commercial MLS website is most recommended for finding commercial real estate listings?

2) What does GRM stand for and what does it mean? Is it a financial figure that should be used as any accurate measure?

3) Define CAP rate. What does it mean? What is the equation? What is the lowest CAP rate you should consider if trying to structure a no-money-down deal?

4) What does "debt service" mean? In commercial real estate, how is it calculated? Monthly? Or annually?

5) What is a seller's agent and how does this differ from a buyer's agent? What is a listing agent? Who does he (or she) work for?

6) What are "proforma" numbers? Why are they not numbers you want to abide by when figuring out property cash flow? Should you consider the listing agent's proforma or simply create your own?

7) Why are "actual" numbers so important?

8) Define what "rent roll" means. How often does it become available?

9) Define DCR or DSCR. What does it mean and why is it important to the lender or bank? What is the minimum that most lenders want to see?

10) As a residential-commercial real estate investor who wants to get the best cash flow, especially coming in with nothing or little down, which "class" properties will you be targeting to get to your maximum cash flow goal?

11) Why should you shy away from Class A properties?

12) Define "unit mix." What is the best unit mix and why? What is traditionally the problem with studio and 1 bedroom/1 bath units?

13) What does "farm" mean? Why is it important to your real estate investing career?

14) Define *effective* income. What does it mean? How is it different than *scheduled* income? Which is the more accurate figure?

15) What is a CA or Confidentiality Agreement?

16) What does "and/or assigns" mean and why should you put this in every LOI or offer you submit?

17) What is the main different between an LOI (Letter of Intent) and an offer? Which is the best one to use and why?

18) What is a contingency? Please explain.

19) What are Proof of Funds? How can you get a POF letter without having any actual liquid assets?

20) What is an MLA? What is the only type of deal that this applies to? Does it apply to other deals?

21) What is the difference between a lease-option and 100% owner financing? Please explain.

22) Define what "replacement reserves" are? Do you know how this may differ from "funded reserves"? If so, please explain.

23) What is an APN? Offer a definition and how it applies to every property in the country.

24) Why is it *not* recommended to use hard money?

25) What are "wet" funds? Is this a loan? When do "wet" funds need to be paid back?

26) The term having "skin in the game" means what exactly?

27) What is a Buyer's Repair Credit? How does this work with DPA? How can you use DPA and a Buyer's Repair Credit to "borrow" the seller's built-in property equity? *(For a video on this topic, visit **www.MonicaMain.com** and click on the "video" link. Look for the DPA video for a full explanation on how this works.)*

28) What is a PMC? Please explain what it stands for and when it is used.

29) Section 8 goes through which government agency?

30) Why are assumable loans next to impossible for an investor with no cash and no credit to work with? What is an alternative to working with these types of loans without having to walk away from the property deal?

31) What is a "lockout"? How does this affect a conventional loan? What is the typical lockout period?

32) Why is a "non-recourse" loan preferred over a "recourse" loan? Why is it harder to get a non-recourse for funded amounts that are less than $1 million on a commercial loan?

Exercise #27
Increasing Your Bottom Line

What's most obvious to people is that in order to make more money with apartment buildings, you simply increase the rents. While this is a great idea in a hot real estate market, it's not always a good idea to start raising rents in an era where unemployment is high and you cannot justify higher rental rates based on higher real estate market fluctuation when the market is, well…not going anywhere. Plus, certain apartment buildings are under rent control. These, of course, are not recommended investments to pick up. If you get stuck with one or a building that is primarily Section 8 then you will be forced to work with raising your bottom line in other ways (which is recommended anyway).

"Value-add" is a term that addresses the questions of: what can you do for your building to increase the bottom-line cash flow by minimizing expenses while increasing property value? Value-add means technically one thing: what can you do to increase the property value to increase cash flow? It means *two* things to me: what can I do to increase property value *and* minimize expenses to increase bottom-line cash flow?

Value-add isn't a matter of throwing in special light switches into each to marginally increase the appraised value of your building because it won't increase your cash flow. If it doesn't increase the cash flow then I don't care about doing it for the building. By adding these light switches, I am increasing my costs to *maybe* increase my appraised value but I'm doing nothing to increase my cash flow because I cannot turn around and rent the unit for a higher rate because of this addition. This is *not* my definition of value-add.

I like value-add ideas that I can implement to make more money right away. Yes, it will cost money to implement the value-add plans but I will make a lot more money on it as time goes along. For example, a value-add would be building a laundry room in a small apartment building where tenants normally have to go offsite to have their laundry washed. Further value-add would be to put soda and snack machines in the laundry room to make extra money. Even further value-add would be to put a pinball and video game in the laundry room to cash in even more.

Value-add could go in the reverse fashion (at least in my definition). I could eliminate my landscaper to have my onsite property manager tend to the lawn, thus saving money and "adding value" to my bottom-line cash flow. I could eliminate having costly flowers planted several times a year and have pretty bushes planted instead; I am adding "value" to the tenants by creating a nicer environment while eliminating an unnecessary and costly expense.

When considering value-add rehab, cosmetic upgrades, or other options, don't do it unless you can see an immediate effect on your cash flow. As with the example of the light switches, make sure it's not a wasteful upgrade that an appraiser will swear will increase your property value but it has *nothing* to do with increasing your bottom-line cash flow. Make sure there is a direct and immediate correlation between the upgrade and the visible cash flow.

This has nothing to do with doing rehab or construction work to get your building in basic functional order. If your building has lost its Certificate of Occupancy (CO) then it is not considered a value-add to do the necessary work to bring the building back up to code through construction work.

Adding a swimming pool *may* be a value-add only if you can attract more tenants at a higher rental rate or keep your occupancy level consistently higher. However, this addition may be too costly in both initial construction and ongoing maintenance (not to mention pool heating bills) to be worth the value-add you originally intended to set in motion. This is something you must be aware of when putting value-add plans in motion.

I had an associate of mine put a local movie studio under contract. It wasn't being sold as a business but rather it was mostly a land deal. It was a small movie studio of about 6 sound stages and a whole lot of acres for back lot filming. Someone savvy with good business acumen could have walked into the deal and gotten it to function as a business by renting out the sound stages to smaller movie productions or to larger studios who needed special back lot scenes to be filmed.

My associate had a business partner who wanted to upgrade the sound stages to a higher form of technology that all the other studios had implemented. I did think this was a great value-add (and probably required to lure business in). The other value-add idea was to bring in some more sound equipment that could be rented by the production companies coming in to rent the sound stages. Again, this was also a great idea because it would increase the businesses overall long-term bottom-line cash flow.

What I didn't agree with was that his business partner wanted to put in a spa including a steam room for the talent that showed up on the lot for filming. This was a bonehead idea because it isn't the studio's job to make the lot a haven for movie stars. The production company involved in using the lot would have to meet the demands of the star(s) with their own provided accommodations. While this was a "value-add" in this person's mind, it wasn't a value-add idea at all. It would have caused a financial loss just in building and operating the spa when it had *no* bottom-line money-making value since it was suggested that it would merely be a benefit for the stars on location. There would be no additional financial compensation the studio would receive for having this spa in place.

Please work through these questions:

1) Take a look at your deals. Find the value-add opportunities in each one. Think outside the box as much as possible and don't limit yourself. Remember, there are sometimes costs in operating the addition to the property (such as a pool) and you have to do the math to determine if it's still going to increase the bottom line…or not. Write down your value-add ideas for each of your properties.

2) List as many value-add ideas as possible. (i.e. Laundry room, soda machines, snack machines, video games, swimming pool to draw in more tenants, build an additional 4-plex on the property for more rental income, build a small toddler park to attract more families; don't forget about the "trade off" and the operations costs of your ideas including the possible legal liabilities, lawsuits, and additional insurances needed to implement your strategies.)

Part IV:
FINDING SUCCESS

Exercise #28
Buckshot Way of Gathering Leads – The Letter Campaign

You can find success in this business by finding properties in the online MLS system, "working" listing agents for "pocket listings" that are not part of the MLS, have access to the asset management department at a bank to gain access to their REO portfolio and, of course, doing a letter campaign to get to those property deals that no other investor will have access to because they aren't for sale yet!

On of the absolute best ways to consistently pack your pipeline full of new deals is by doing a letter campaign at least once a month. As the market heats up (as it will in the next couple of years), it will become more difficult to compete with other investors (especially with money down) on the listings nationally available to every investor on the MLS. Even now during our slow market, you can find sellers that will be agreeable to partial owner financing (even if you have to use the transactional funding and "buyer's repair credit" method to close the deal).

Your first step is to get some kind of subscription to gain access to letter campaign leads. You can do this through a service called Prospect Now (formerly Lead-Trac). They can allow you access to thousands of commercial real estate owners in a single county for a small monthly (or annual) fee. (If you want to get a discount from their service fee, call them on the phone and use the code "MM" or "Monica Main.") Their website is www.ProspectNow.com. It may seem limiting to only gain access to one county at a time but you can change your county once a month. This will give you an advantage of working fast to farm a single county in the first month then switch to a new county in the next month. This service requires a one-year subscription commitment so you will have to be a "serious" investor to take the jump.

Here are some rules for letter campaigns:

1) Do not refer to needing 100% owner financing or any kind of seller carry-back in letter.
2) Make sure you indicate that you are not a real estate or listing agent trying to trick them into getting their business.
3) Make it clear that you are a fellow investor who is actively seeking and purchasing property in the immediate area of their property. You are trying to save them the high commissions in using a real estate agent to list and sell their property when most sit on their ass and do nothing to earn the commission anyway (other than listing the property in LoopNet).
4) Indicate that you will make them a "offer they can't refuse" within 48 hours provided that the numbers work out for you.
5) Make sure you have a template or script to follow before the calls start coming in so that you are prepared to handle questions while gathering all the information you need to make an accurate analysis of their deal.
6) Understand that even if the property owner presses you for whether you will be asking for any kind of "creative" or owner financing, you are *not* to verbally discuss these details on the phone. Leave it to your offer to do the "talking" for you!
7) Don't consider doing "follow up" mailings in the same area unless you are getting a minimum of a 15% to 20% response off of your gathered mailing list; if you do get

this kind of response then consider doing 2 follow up mailings about 5 – 8 weeks apart.

8) Ideally you will be sending out at least 100 - 150 pieces of mail per week. You should be sending out a minimum of 500 pieces of mail per month to a single county.

9) Do *not* try to use LoopNet.com to gather leads for your letter campaigns by looking up the "property record" information on each listing to view the owner's name and address. LoopNet.com will discover that you are doing this and they will terminate your account, even if you are a *Premium Member*. It is much too time consuming to gather leads this way anyway.

10) Try to give them access to you directly (like a cell phone) or have a live answering service address the phone calls. Don't sent them to your home phone or have a cheesy answering machine (or voice mail) message for them to hear because you will lose a lot of leads this way.

While I'm in the flow of having you do this assignment, I want you to start thinking about you developing your "template" or script for when property owners call you so you will feel more prepared. Here is a listing of the things you will have to ask them when they call:

1) Property address.
2) Number of units.
3) Unit mix.
4) Total square footage of livable space.
5) Total property acres.
6) Property APN.
7) Year built.
8) Current occupancy level.
9) Gross Operating Income (GOI) for the previous fiscal year.
10) Net Operating Expenses (NOE) for the previous fiscal year.
11) How much equity do they have in the building?
12) Why are they considering selling?
13) Is their property listed with an agent in an active listing?
14) Do they have an assumable loan? If so, what is the balance and what are the terms?

Then end the conversation with a simple "Thank you" and "I'll respond to you in the next couple of days with an official offer if the numbers work out for me."

Pretty simple, don't you think? Don't worry. None of these property owners will bite. They may try to press you for information about you and demand to see POF, a preapproval letter, or your financials but you need to explain that you are going to be using a conventional lender and it's only their business to see financial information.

By the way, if anyone ever asks you for a preapproval letter from a lender, you need to know that preapproval letters are not given out on commercial properties. They are given out on residential purchases only because the amount of the loan is qualified based on your personal credit and income. Since commercial property is handled much differently in that the property's income and expenses "qualify" the loan, a lender cannot even start the process of issuing a preapproval until you have an actual property deal to work with!

Here are some sample letters to use for your letter campaigns:

I Want Your Property and I'm Willing to Make You An Offer You CAN'T REFUSE...

YOUR NAME HERE
ADDRESS
CITY/STATE/ZIP
PHONE NUMBER

PROPERTY OWNER
ADDRESS.
CITY/STATE/ZIP

Dear PROPERTY OWNER,

I'm interested in purchasing your building at [ADDRESS]. And I'm willing to make you an offer you CAN'T REFUSE within the next 48 hours. **GUARANTEED!**

I am actively investing in buildings in the immediate area of your building located at the above address and your property fits the exact criteria of what I'm looking for. Your property is perfect for what I'm looking for and I'm willing to make you an offer you can't refuse.

Everyone comes to a time in their lives where they want to get rid of their property for one reason or another. I may be jumping the gun and assuming that you want to sell (when you really don't) but if you've even had a remote fleeting thought of selling, give me a call. There's no point in dealing with an undeserving real estate agent who wants to bleed you dry in commissions for barely doing any work when we can cut out the "middle man" altogether. This will save you money and make the deal even sweeter, don't you think?

I am prepared to make a quick offer and I would like to close on your schedule, whether you want to close within 30 days or if you would prefer a longer escrow period. I'll leave it completely up to you.

By the way, just in case you think I'm a real estate agent trying to swindle my into your life, I can assure you that I am a fellow investor and NOT someone looking to list your property.

Please contact me at today so that I can begin putting together my written offer which I'll be prepared to present to you within 48 hours. Call me right now at [PHONE NUMBER]. This is my personal direct line so you'll reach me immediately.

I look forward to hearing from you in the next few minutes!

Sincerely,
YOUR SIGNATURE

P.S. I'm going to make this a win-win deal for both of us. I think you'll really like the offer I put together and my offer price on your building. Give me a call so that we can discuss the details: [PHONE NUMBER]

Your Property Will Lose 9.72% in Value Within the Next 8 Months!

Think the Economy Is Getting Better? Think Again!

Dear PROPERTY OWNER,

Right now your property is worth [$XXXXXX]. But it won't be for long!

It will be worth almost 10% less than what it appraises out at right now in less than a year from now!

Do you think I'm full of it? Right? You don't think I'm serious…or you think that this is some kind of gimmick or scam. But what if I'm not? Then what?

Why am I sending you this letter? I want to buy your property for what it's worth RIGHT NOW before the market throws you another curve ball. I am a real estate investor just like you who wants to buy your property and I'm serious about wanting to offer you [$ XXXXXX] for your property located at [PROPERTY ADDRESS].

Listen, the economy isn't great right now and if you plan on selling your building in the near future, expect it to sit on the market for quite awhile before getting any interested (and legitimate) buyers to submit an offer to you. On top of that, you'll probably be using a listing agent who is going to rob you blind in commissions…and who wants that?

Give me a call right now so that we can discuss the details! You can reach me at [PHONE NUMBER] which is my direct line.

I'm waiting for your phone call!

Sincerely,

YOUR SIGNATURE

YOUR NAME HERE

P.S. Why hold onto a property that isn't performing the way you think it should or to continue dealing with nightmare tenants that are sucking the life out of you? Cash out and enjoy the money…or get a bigger building and really start raking in the cash flow!

P.P.S. CALL ME <u>TODAY</u> AND LET'S GET THIS PROCESS ROLLING: [PHONE NUMBER]

Hiring a Real Estate Agent to Sell Your Property Will Cost You a <u>Minimum</u> of $30,000!

And Why Give That Kind of Money to a Joker Who Merely Throws Your Property Up on LoopNet.com?

RE: Property located at [PROPERTY ADDRESS]

Dear PROPERTY OWNER,

The thought of trading your burdensome building in for the cash (or to trade up to a higher cash flowing building) probably has crossed your mind several times in the past couple of years. Hasn't it?

The problem? Real estate agents really suck! They are arrogant, undeserving blood-suckers who will get tens of thousands of dollars (if not more) for little work, time, and effort. And who wants to give them the money when you can stuff it into your pocket! ***Right?***

Listen, I want your property! And I'm willing to do almost anything to get it! I'm even willing to offer you MORE than market value AND I'm willing to present an offer to you within the next 48 hours! GUARANTEED!

No, I'm not a listing agent. I'm an investor JUST LIKE YOU who understands that we all want to throw in the towel for greener pastures. Maybe that time has arrived for you but you've balked at the idea of listing your property because of the high commissions, the crappy real estate market, or the difficulty in selling your property for a price other than the ridiculous low-ball offers that investors are insulting property owners with nowadays.

Here's the deal that you can't refuse: I want to give you an incredible, mind-blowing price on your property…I may offer you MORE than you possibly expect or consider reasonable. AND I'm willing to make an offer on your building within 48 hours.

Give me a call right now so we can talk about your property. I want to get a written offer into your hands within the next 48 hours. ***Why waste another second?*** I'll be expecting your call. Call me at [PHONE NUMBER].

Sincerely,

YOUR SIGNATURE

[YOUR NAME HERE]

P.S. I am prepared to make you an offer you can't refuse within the next 48 hours on your property! Call me right now at [PHONE NUMBER]!

LAST CHANCE!

I Want to Offer You [$ XXXXXX] for the Property at [Street Address] And You Would Be <u>CRAZY</u> If You Turned Me Down!

YOUR NAME
ADDRESS
CITY/STATE/ZIP
PHONE NUMBER

PROPERTY OWNER
ADDRESS
CITY/STATE/ZIP

Dear PROPERTY OWNER,

Remember I told you that I wanted to make you an offer you couldn't refuse?

Strangely, you didn't respond to me…

Then I figured out why! *You think I'm full of it.* You don't think I'm serious…or you think that this is some kind of gimmick or scam.

I can assure you that I am a real estate investor just like you who wants to buy your property and I'm serious about wanting to offer you [$ XXXXXX] for your property located at [PROPERTY ADDRESS].

Listen, the economy isn't great right now and if you plan on selling your building in the near future, expect it to sit on the market for quite awhile before getting any interested (and legitimate) buyers to submit an offer to you. On top of that, you'll probably be using a listing agent who is going to rob you blind in commissions…and who wants that?

Give me a call right now so that we can discuss the details! You can reach me at [PHONE NUMBER] which is my direct line.

I'm waiting for your phone call!

Sincerely,

YOUR SIGNATURE

P.S. Why hold onto a property that isn't performing the way you think it should or to continue dealing with nightmare tenants that are sucking the life out of you? Cash out and enjoy the money…or get a bigger building and really start raking in the cash flow!

P.P.S. CALL ME <u>TODAY</u> AND LET'S GET THIS PROCESS ROLLING: [PHONE NUMBER]

1) Now it's your turn to write your own letter. Using one of the templates above, write a letter for your own campaign by starting with a headline. Include the keywords I have above. Make sure you use a headline at the top. Do not put the name of your LLC or your business address where the headline is supposed to be. Many investors make this mistake then wonder why they get no response. Be sure to use a headline instead of your business name at top. Write at least 5 sample headlines below:

2) Read through my sample letters again. What keywords have you read in the letters that stand out to you? Put yourself in a property owner's shoes. Which keywords would get you to pick up the phone? Which items in the letters are boring, irrelevant, or elements that you would not respond to (or like) as an investor reading the letter about your property that you own?

3) Are you ready to become a serious real estate investor? If so, you'll need to get some business cards. You'll especially need these if you plan on doing a successful letter campaign. I recommend a company called **www.PrintsMadeEasy.com** because they allow you to use their online templates to quickly create very professional looking business cards within minutes.

Exercise #29
Scouting Property

One of my recommendations to "build your pot" so that you have cash for your property deals is to find property for other investors for money. You can either do this with the referral fee method or you can flip the property to an end-buyer by taking a profit out of the middle. This is a lucrative way to raise money but it can be difficult for those who don't like to get out there and hustle or who don't have good written communication skills.

After reading my chapter on bird-dogging, you should have been able to determine by now whether this is a job you are up to doing...or not. Bird-dogging is definitely not for everyone. It's not a matter of finding a property listing on the MLS and then sending the link to someone then wondering when you can get paid. You don't deserve any money for simply finding a property MLS link because everyone has instant access to the online MLS. Just because you know how to use the Internet doesn't allow you to get paid for finding a property listing that is available for everyone in the world to see instantaneously.

A property scout not only has to find properties but also needs to find the "don't want" deals then build them into deals that have huge potential. This will mean that you will have to be able to create a solid business plan and possibly a PowerPoint presentation to show investors so that they may see the future cash flow potential as you do. If you don't think you have the skill in the written communication department then you can either choose to build this skill or forget about being a property scout altogether.

Please read my lengthy bird-dogging chapter in *Apartment Building Millionaire*. After you read this chapter, you can decide if this is up your alley...or not. You are not a failure if you find that property scouting isn't something you think you can do. Just understand that there is work involved and it's not as simple as a few clicks of the mouse to be a successful bird-dog. Instead there is a lot more involved and anyone can learn how to do this if they understand that outstanding written communication is a must.

Take the time to answer these questions:

1) After completing your reading of the bird-dogging chapter, do you think this is something you can successfully do? If so, please explain the virtues within yourself that can allow you to be a successful bird-dog. If not, please explain why you believe you won't be able to make bird-dogging work for you.

2) Which type of bird-dogging would you like to do: referral fee or flipping? Explain your answer.

3) The first thing you must do when deciding to become a bird-dog is to find a lucrative area to farm deals. You have probably done this already. However, you need to understand that you can expand your areas of search to areas that maybe wouldn't have worked for you financially but it can work for an investor who will either provide 100% cash or will offer a huge down payment to buy the property. This changes the "playing field" because you may venture into areas that may otherwise have been personally off-limits to you as an investor investing in the deals yourself. Which areas in the country may you consider for bird-dogging deals for other investors that you may have determined to be unsuitable for your cash flow requirements in your own research process? Please make sure that the areas you do find bird-dog deals and has a solid demographics and employment rate. These areas must also have annual population *expansion* rather than contraction; the area must also have *diverse* industry rather than *singular* industry (like Detroit, for instance).

4) Start locating deals in that area. You may want to work up some basic CFEs both for current cash flow and a future "proforma" projection to extend out annually for the next 3 years. You are looking for properties with a lot of "value-add" potential. You are *not* looking for the property that is 95% to 100% occupied and has recently underwent hundreds of thousands of dollars in renovations or rehab. There isn't that much potential in a property that someone else has already "fixed." Look for the "don't want" properties in an area that has an expanding population and find the potential in the property. What have you been able to locate? Explain the property deals and what their potential may be. The property may look like a disaster but you need to throw the rose-colored glasses on and see the potential instead of what is there now and then you will have to have the magical talent to make others see the potential as well.

5) Once you have been able to find some hot property deals, you can begin "posting" to see if other investors will be interested in your possible deal. You can look at signing up with places like **www.Breadstreet.com**. These services do charge monthly fees so you need to be fairly sure that you are serious about doing this before committing to this monthly expense. Take a look at other postings. Look at the ones that would excite you if you were an investor looking for a lucrative project with a high Return on Investment (ROI). You may also want to take a look at www.LoopNet.com and their "Big Board." Write down a few of these postings that you find to be the ones that would have very powerful wording to prompt any potential investor to respond.

6) One of the ways you will make it in this business as a bird-dog is by getting investors to seek out or flip property deals for. You can advertise in places like the LoopNet Big Board (which currently costs $149 per month). Here is an ad that is quite successful that a bird-dog has written and it runs month after month quite successfully:

APARTMENT BUILDING INVESTORS...

Tired of "wholesalers" and agents who send you cut and pasted website links of listings with "deals" that don't meet any of your investing criteria? If you have the cash to put properties on escrow fast and the financing resources to close, I'll send you deals based on your guidelines, with all the financial analysis done, supporting documents and an LOI already accepted by the seller with terms such as partial owner financing and no down payment as part of the transaction. Contact me today.

The reason I believe this ad is so successful is because it "talks" to the investor. I have a bird-dogging program where I allow qualified students who enroll into my exclusive program to give me bird-dog deals for a referral fee. I find myself very frustrated because of the issues that the writer of the ad above describes. I routinely get cut-and-pasted links to LoopNet or other MLS sites with skimpy information about the property and none of my criteria has been met or respectfully considered. It's as if the bird-dog is saying, "Here's the link I found on LoopNet.com. Now, where is my 3% for 'finding' you this deal?" This is why I would definitely jump on the ad above to see if I could find a bird-dog who is willing to listen to my well-laid-out listing of criteria and follow up with some deals that I'm really looking for.

If you can write an ad as the one above, you will also do very well as a bird-dog with a boatload of investors who will pay you handsomely for your deals. Write an ad like the one above and see if you can make it better or more tantalizing:

7) One of the requirements that you'll have to overcome is when sellers of property deals ask you for Proof of Funds (POF) to put a deal under contract. This requires you to get quick POF from a transactional funding company upon request. Go to **www.Coastal-Funding.com** and get a quick POF for an amount of less than $1 million. I want you to experience how easy it is to "prove" to someone that you have the funds to close the deal. Report your experience with getting this proof below: was it easy? Hard? Did you do it successfully and fast like I said you would be able to?

8) Out of the deals you were able to find, can you write a posting that you think you can attract investors for? If so, please write your sample ads based on real deals you have found. Your postings should not exceed 4 sentences. Make them powerful.

Exercise #30
Writing a Business Plan

For real estate a business plan is much different than that of one for a business. A business plan for a business consists of an overall view of a business present and future. A real estate business plan is supposed to talk only about a *specific property deal* and *not* your overall "business" plan as a real estate investor (i.e. how many buildings you want to acquire in 10 years, etc.) You will have to get very good at writing business plans if you want to be a successful bird-dog or if you want to provide a lender/bank with convincing details as to why they should lend you money on a commercial building when you have little or no management experience.

I have a real estate business plan writing software called Real Estate Proposal Pro. It's the only software on the market for real estate proposals and business plans. All other template business plan software focuses on an overall business which is too complicated to use for a single real estate deal. For more information about my Real Estate Proposal Pro Software, visit **www.RealEstateProposalSoftware.com**. It will help you streamline the process much quicker than trying to use a general run-of-the-mill business plan software.

Again, writing a business plan or proposal on a property deal is not just for bird-dog deals. All lenders are now asking for something called an "executive summary" which is an overall summary of a longer business plan. Some lenders, especially private money, are asking for an entire business plan, especially if you cannot show prior management experience or a management resume.

If you plan on being a successful investor who will successfully get bank or private mortgages then you will need to learn how to write a business plan.

Please work through the listing of questions to put you on the right track to writing a solid business plan:

1) For an executive summary, please answer these questions about your property deal:

    a. What is your personal investment history?

    b. Why are you investing in real estate and what are your expectations?

    c. What is your main objective? To accumulate wealth in the form of real property? To establish a steady stream of passive income?

d. What investments do you currently hold?

e. If you have a spouse or a team, identify them and their respective roles and expectations.

2) Please answer these questions on market analysis and the farm area you are currently planning on purchasing property in:

a. Where is your target market?

b. What property types will you acquire? Multi-family? Commercial?

c. What is the asking price of the property?

d. What type of buyer/renter are you targeting?

e. What are the area demographics including unemployment rates (in comparison to the rest of the U.S.)? What is the major industry there? What is the average annual population growth by year for the past 5 years?

3) Answer these questions about acquisition and rehab (if needed);

    a. What will the acquisition cost be (purchase price)?

    b. Is there rehab needed?

    c. How will you estimate repairs accurately?

    d. How will you control holding costs?

    e. What is your game plan for a rehab?

    f. What repairs do you tackle first, second, last?

    g. To what level of quality do you rehab a property?

4) Answer these questions about the management strategy:

    a. Who will rent out your properties?

    b. What will make your property rent faster than the competition?

    c. What if the units won't rent?

    d. Are you prepared to rent out the units yourself?

e. Do you have creative marketing methods to attract tenants? If so, please indicate.

f. How will you determine your rental rate per unit?

g. What about closing costs, taxes, property insurance, liability insurance, fines, permits, etc.? Have these been covered in your cash flow analysis?

h. How can you be assured of a profit?

i. What makes your property better than the competition (i.e., the other apartment units on the market)?

5) Answer these questions about current and future financial projections:

a. What is the current cash flow of the property based on actual numbers?

b. Will you be putting any money down of your own? If so, what are the sources of these funds?

c. What do the future projections of this property deal look like? Please indicate with charts and numbers. What assumptions are you making when projecting future funding needs?

d. What are your figures for gross revenues and net income in past 3 years?

e. What are your figures for gross revenues and net income for the next 3 years?

f. How are you arriving at your future figures? Based on what data?

g. What is the total amount that will be needed for rehab or cosmetic upgrades?

h. What are the "value-add" opportunities in the property deal?

i. Do you have charts and graphs to illustrate your financial history and future projections?

6) Please answer these questions about your exit strategy:

    a. What do you plan on doing with this property? Buy and hold? Buy and flip? Please explain.

    b. If you plan on flipping, what are you going to do between the time of acquisition and the time of flip? Rehab? Lease-up?

    c. When will you flip the property? After how many months or years?

    d. If you plan on buying and holding, what type of management will you put into place? Please explain.

Exercise #31
Setting Up Your Business

You need an LLC in order to operate a business in real estate. Your initial LLC should be in your home state. This will be your "umbrella" LLC. Each LLC that is purchased (either in your home state or out of state) will have be designated for each property deal you do. Your main LLC will be the "single-member" on each additional LLC you start for each property deal you do. The LLC structure is the best way to protect yourself while maximizing your tax benefits as a real estate investor.

Here is the recommended structure:

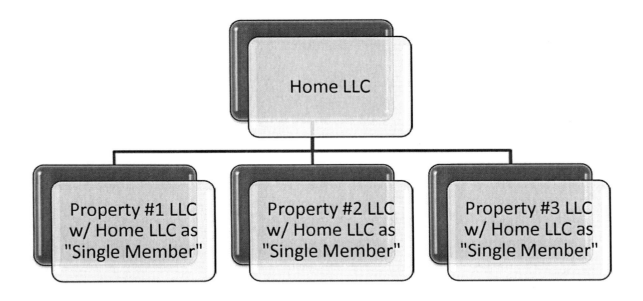

Each property LLC will be in the home state of the property transaction. For example, if you live in Texas then your "home" LLC that will operate as an umbrella at the top will be a Texas LLC. It will then become the sole and single member of each additional property LLC you do for different deals. However, the new LLCs that are designated for different property deals will be in the home of the state you are purchasing property or where the property is physically located. If your properties are in different states then you will need 3 LLCs under your home LLC.

Pretend that your property deals are in the following states: Georgia (#1), Florida (#2), and Alabama (#3). Pretend that your home state is Texas. Here is how your structure may look:

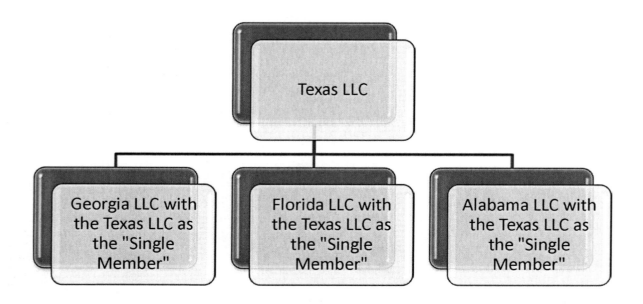

Your umbrella LLC should *never* own any property. If you decide to purchase a property in your home state, consider getting another LLC for the property deal so you don't expose your umbrella LLC legally on a home state property deal. You will do the same thing as outlined above where your new Texas LLC will have your original Texas LLC as the "single member" of the new LLC if you live in Texas, as an example.

You are probably wondering what "single member" means. You have to remember that an LLC is considered an "entity" just like a live, breathing human being is. Therefore, the "single member" is the umbrella LLC and your name is not on the LLC anywhere except as a "manager" who can sign on behalf of the umbrella LLC. You want your LLCs to have a single member on the paperwork so that you may have the profits from the property "sift down" to your home state LLC. Then you will file the appropriate tax paperwork for your home state LLC while taking all of the profits on your personal tax return without filing more paperwork than you have to. The second you start adding partners in on any of your property deal LLCs then you will have to file much more paperwork to the IRS because it changes the tax filing status of the LLC. This is why you should always choose "single member" and leave off a ton of people; this will simplify and streamline your tax obligations.

If you are a husband/wife team, only put both of you as active and equal members on your home LLC *only*. Then all of your "underling" LLCs will use the *home* LLC as the *sole single member* but it will "include" both partners in the husband/wife team. (This same strategy applied to any partnership and *not* just for husband/wife teams only.)

By the way, if you are purchasing a bunch of smaller buildings in the same state that all have between 5 and 20 units each (or even smaller if you are doing duplexes, triplexes, and "quads"), you can put 3 - 5 properties under the same state LLC so you aren't wasting a bunch of money opening up new LLCs for each one. All the "experts" (who are usually corporation attorneys) recommend a new LLC for each property but this really isn't necessary. The issue is, of course, taxes. You *cannot* blend your income and expenses on all of your property deals because, if you sell one, you will have a problem giving a potential buyer the right cash flow information.   Use Intuit's *Real Estate Solutions Software.*   Intuit created Quicken and QuickBooks. They have a "QuickBooks" for real estate (*Real Estate Solutions Software*) and this software will help you keep the books on your entire "empire" while keeping each building separated for tax and profit/loss statement reasons.

Finally, you will have to name all of your LLCs "the same." Here's how it may look:

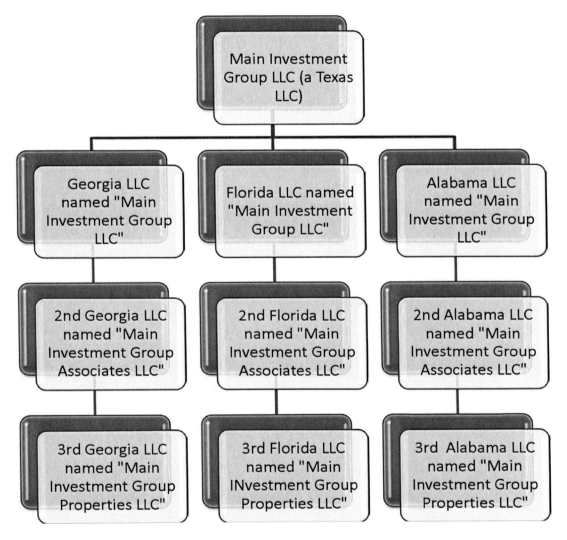

You will do this because of the "bank account" issue. Since the *Patriot Act* came into place, it's difficult to get an out of state bank account for business purposes unless you can show residency there. You would use your "main" home state LLC to open your bank account and you will funnel all of the rental payments into the same "account system" at the bank. Since each LLC has its own EIN, each time you applied for the new LLCs EIN you should have "tied" your home state EIN into the new LLCs EIN application (instead of putting your personal Social Security Number information. This will make it all legal from the IRS's standpoint because the home state LLCs EIN is on the EIN applications for all of the "underling" LLCs. Since each LLC is a "single member" then this allows the profits from each underling to flow down to your home state LLC anyway. It's all seamless, really.

When you open up your initial home LLC bank account, the first account will be called the "main" account. You can open up separate checking accounts within the same "umbrella" for each of your properties. You can name them, sort of like children. This is how it may look:

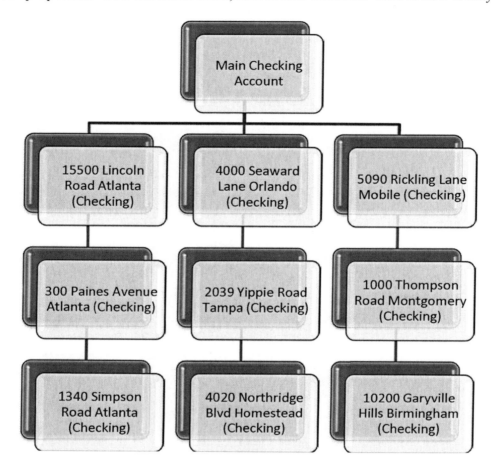

All of the checks from tenants will show your main LLC which, in my example, is "Main Investment Group." (Now you know why all the LLCs you have must be named the *same name* or some variation thereof.) This will allow you to deposit the checks into the same account system but in its own separate checking account for the property.

Now, go through these questions:

1) Do you have a home state LLC? If so, please include the name. If not, please consider starting one today!

2) How many buildings (or units) in a single area would it make you comfortable having under one LLC? (Remember, you shouldn't add out of state properties into an LLC that is not for the state where the property is located. Don't add a Georgia property to a Texas LLC with a Texas property, for instance.)

3) Does the action plan including the hierarchy I outlined above make sense to you? (If not, please read through my chapter in *Apartment Building Millionaire* on LLCs for clarification.)

Exercise #32
Building Business Credit

Business credit is becoming a requirement if you want to ensure your future as a commercial real estate investor. Banks are starting to look seriously at solid business credit, especially after the mortgage meltdown we recently experienced. If you have a current home state LLC then you can begin the process of building business credit. Please go through the business credit building chapter in *Apartment Building Millionaire* before beginning to understand this process.

Answer the following questions:

1) How "aged" is your LLC or corporation? (In what year was it formed?)

2) Do you have any open trade accounts with vendors under your LLCs EIN?

3) Indicate your trade accounts, if any. If you have none, consider getting an Office Depot card, a gas card, and a couple of other trade accounts right now.

4) Do you have a DNB (Dun & Bradstreet) number? If so, please list it below. If not, you will need to wait until you have 3 trade accounts before starting a DNB profile.

Exercise #33
Building Your Real Estate Empire

I want to test your knowledge on the remaining chapters of Apartment Building Millionaire from 9 through the end. I will be asking you a series of questions to test your knowledge. Please focus on chapters 9 and on to answer these questions.

Let us begin:

1) Define "earnest money deposit."

2) Do you have earnest money for deals? If so, explain what you have.

3) Generally, what is the average earnest money deposit as far as percentage?

4) Define "bird-dog." Is this something you are interested in doing?

5) What is a "double" or "back-to-back" close? Please define.

6) What is a 1031 Exchange?

7) What are the best types of properties to offer to investors?

8) What is an "exit strategy"?

9) Define "short sale."

10) How do you calculate an ROI?

11) Why is building business credit so important to a real estate investor?

12) What is an "angel investor"? Please explain.

13) What is the best way to raise private money?

14) What are the elements you should have in a business plan for an equity partner?

15) Why is getting an LLC for real estate the best asset protection and tax recommendation?

16) Define "verifiable financials."

17) What is the difference between "title" and "escrow"?

18) What legal skills are you looking for when finding an attorney?

19) How can a residential real estate agent be used when renting out units?

20) What is the best way to handle evictions?

21) Can a management company every be used? If so, please explain how.

22) What is a "vig"?

23) Define "loss-to-lease."

24) Define "capital additions."

Exercise #34
Building Your Real Estate Empire

Now is the time for you to create a solid action plan. You should already be well-grounded in the farming area that you are currently working in. Hopefully you have been able to put a deal under contract by now. If not then you really need to crack the whip on yourself and get rolling with your business.

I want you to outline your own action plan and goal list below. Your time in thoroughly outlining where you see yourself in 5 years from now, how many units you have, where the properties are located, and what your monthly bottom-line cash flow is. Now is the time to drive your visual home then to make it a priority to make it happen in your life.

Here we go:

1) Have you been able to put any deals into contract right now?

2) How many offers have you submitted so far?

3) If you are having difficulty with this process, what seems to be the "snag"? Explain.

4) Please fill in the chart below:

	Number of Units	Area(s) of Investing	Cash Flow Goal
12 Months			
24 Months			
36 Months			
48 Months			
60 Months			

5) What do you believe is your biggest obstacle to getting deals done?

6) What have you been doing daily to become a successful investor? Explain.

7) What do you need to add to your daily schedule to move forward as an investor?

8) What additional education do you need to become successful? Please explain.

Exercise #35
Get Your Ass Out There and Do It!

I have dealt with tens of thousands of students over the past several years and fear seems to be the main thing that keeps hindering people from moving forward. For my mentorship groups I allow for a 60 minute phone consulting session with me personally. The same thing I hear over and over again is a long string of "what if" scenarios, many of which aren't likely to happen or aren't even *possible* to take place. Yet people will keep themselves up in the middle of the night talking themselves out of doing this at a time when they are psychologically the weakest because they are physically and mentally exhausted.

Listen, I am considered an "expert" on many levels but I find that sometimes I start the whole "what if" questionnaire with myself at 2 AM when I start working on a project that is out of my "comfort level." This is when I am physically and mentally drained and my "angel" and "devil" within my own head is working against me (usually collectively together).

I find that I have to force myself through a new type of project while listening to my gut. This is the hard part because I have to make sure that when I am shying away from a deal, I have to determine that it's my gut telling me no (which I should listen to) vs. my brain telling me not to because I'm not comfortable (which I *shouldn't* listen to).

Here's the best visual I can give to you that will make sense and something you should remember whenever you are pushing the envelope on yourself. Look at this picture:

You can see that there is fog up ahead. Your job is to only concentrate on the portion of the road you can see now and ignore what's *possibly* in the fog way up there! If you fear the fog and pull over to turn around then you'll *never* get to the destination ahead.

Don't worry about the "what ifs" of the trip. What if there is an accident in the fog? What if someone hits you in the fog? What if you get lost? What if, what if, what if...

Leave it alone. Period. Otherwise you will never get anywhere worthwhile in life by living in your comfort zone.

My most successful students are those who are uneducated and some with lower-than-average IQs. My doctors, dentists, lawyers, engineers, and anyone with a Master's Degree usually ends up doing nothing with this. I have so many doctors that I work with who I know will be working for the rest of their lives because they won't have enough in retirement to support their higher-than-standard lifestyle but they are unwilling to make a move out of fear. My "dumb" ones move forward like a fearless puppy because they don't let their brain overanalyze a deal to death. They move forward, make some errors, move on, and get deals under their belts.

If you are one of the "smart" ones then you need to lose your "over analytical" ability and be smart about the deal but lose the fear. If you are a "dumb" one then *congratulations* because you are about to get very rich as a real estate investor!

Only worry about the two steps in front of you. Everything else will fall into place. Learn how to *trust* that the net will appear when you take the leap.

If you have any questions for me, contact me at **monica@monicamain.com**.

See you at the top!

Your mentor,

Monica Main

Monica Main's Products & Services

For a complete catalog of products and services, please visit **www.MonicaMain.com**.

Apartment Building Cash Flow System – Monica's signature real estate system that every beginning real estate investor should start with. Thousands of students have benefited from this incredible, well-laid-out, investing system with precise little-known strategies that any new real estate investor can use to gain wealth through real estate. For course information, visit **www.ApartmentBuildingCashFlow.com**. To join her 8-week step-by-step mentorship group that boasts an outstanding success rate in helping new investors get a building under contract and into escrow within 8 weeks, visit **www.MonicaMainMentorship.com**.

Build Business Credit *FAST!* – Discover how to get and use corporate credit to finance real estate deals, lease cars, get high-limit credit cards and unsecured loans. Not only can you learn how to access millions of dollars in business credit, you can also quickly fix your personal credit without getting ripped off by "services" that never help you do anything. Course and mentorship group programs available. For complete course information to start building solid credit, please visit **www.SecretstoBusinessCredit.com**. For step-by-step credit-building mentorships, please visit **www.BusinessCreditMentorship.com**.

Bird –Dogging Bonanza – If you want to make money in commercial real estate but aren't quite ready to do your first deals yet then you can "bird-dog" for others while getting paid. How does this work? Find lucrative property deals for investors and "flip" the deal or get paid a referral fee. For course information, visit **www.BirdDoggingOpportunity.com**. For the 8-week mentorship group, visit **www.BirdDogMentorship.com**.

Foreclosure Secrets – If you want to make money in foreclosures, don't consider single-family homes. Get involved in apartment building foreclosures. You can cash in big by getting low-priced property deals by dealing with the banks directly. For course information, visit **www.ApartmentBuildingForeclosures.com**. For information on the step-by-step 8-week mentorship program, visit **www.REOMentorship.com**.

Commercial Cash Flow – Not everyone wants to invest in residential-commercial (apartment building) properties. Some people would like to take on the highly profitable, lower maintenance world of commercial real estate including retail strip malls, industrial/warehouse space, and office buildings. Discover the world of "triple net" where you can lease your units to business tenants that pay all expenses including "CAM" (Common Area Maintenance) fees so you can minimize your expenses (including property taxes) and maximize on your income with stable long-term commercial tenants. For course information, please visit **www.CommercialCashFlowPro.com**.

Wealth Attraction Secrets – In order to become successful in any endeavor, you must "clear your mind" of past negative programming and open up your future for super success and massive amounts of prosperity. It's no accident that people who are wealthy are rich for a reason. And you can be wealthy too. Most self-help information doesn't reveal the true details you need in order to become successful financially while having a direct relationship with business and investing. Monica can show you never-before-revealed secrets to quickly ridding all negativity you have with money while placing you on the fast track to financial success by allowing you to tap into your "flow" of money...*AND FAST!* For more information about her outstanding course, visit **www.UltimateWealthAttraction.com**.

The $74,000 a Month Secret – Monica Main's most successful student Andrew Shaw reveals details about how he went from broke to making $74,000 a month in passive income in 18 months. He also reveals a lending source that gives a 75% LTV on a first-position mortgage by using private seller financing (which lenders typically don't allow anymore). All the details about how he makes money including his secret resource are shared in his course: **www.74KSecret.com**.

Viper Wealth Membership – Monica's newest release; a monthly membership including a physical newsletter, 8-hour call-in days, Webinars, audio seminars, news about the commercial real estate market, new lenders and money resources, and much more. For more information, visit **www.ViperWealth.com**.

Monica Main Seminars – At least twice annually Monica holds a 3-Day Boot Camp Seminar Event. You definitely don't want to miss out on her dynamic approach to teaching with her unique gift in making everything understandable, easy, and step-by-step. She doesn't believe in putting on an event that is a "sell-a-thon" as most "gurus" do. Instead, she offers 3 days of nothing but solid information. She is also going to start doing 5-Day Boot Camp Seminar Events. For more information including the dates of her next event, please visit **www.MonicaMainSeminars.com**.

Boot Camp Seminar Audio/Video – Sometimes it's not realistic to be able to hop on an airplane to see Monica speak live. It can be too costly, inconvenient, or just not possible at this stage in your life. This doesn't mean you should miss out on the valuable information she imparts with, especially since each of her events offer different, new, and cutting-edge information that's usually never been revealed before in any of her other materials. If you have missed out on her last event, consider getting the complete audio and video set including transcripts at **www.BootCampSeminarVideos.com**.

Grant Writer Pro Software – This software is a two-fold program for Windows. It is a tutorial program to assist an investor in locating the latest grant opportunities through the government and it also guides the investor through the process of writing and submitting a grant application. For more information, visit **www.GrantWriterPro2.com**.

Online Mentorship Groups – Monica Main has exclusive mentorship groups for apartment building acquisitions, REO foreclosure acquisitions, bird-dogging, advanced and business credit. These are done 100% online and are over the course of 8 weeks (except for the *Build Business Credit FAST Group* which is longer). Her past groups have had a high success rate of up to 75% of her graduating students having successfully put deals under contract by the end of the 8-week session; they would close escrow shortly thereafter on their property deals. Her business credit mentorship has guided some of her students to build up to $500,000 in *unsecured* business credit before the group ended. Getting daily step-by-step instruction is extremely powerful for ultimate success. These mentorships also include one-on-one sessions with Monica directly. For more information about her mentorship groups including start dates, visit **www.MonicaMainMentorships.com**.

Offer Writer Pro Software – Sometimes beginning investors struggle with writing out a professional-looking offer or LOI that will get a response from the listing agent or seller. Any mistake in the structuring of the financing, legalese, or lingo will not get a response or will be rejected without further consideration. This could mean the difference between winning out in a battle for a multi-million dollar property with a huge monthly cash flow or losing the property while becoming the laughing stock of the entire listing agent's real estate office. You shouldn't take that kind of risk. For more information, visit **www.OfferWriterPro.com**.

Real Estate Proposal Pro Software – A serious investor who hopes to raise private funds and/or impress a lender to approve conventional funding on a deal needs to write a property-specific business plan. Using a boilerplate business plan software is *not* going to cut it. An investor needs a software that will allow for the details of a specific property to be highlighted. This is unlike anything that is currently available on the open market for software. For more information, visit **www.RealEstateProposalSoftware.com**

Real Estate Cash Flow Analyzer (RECFA) Software – This is for the serious investor who wants to move one step deeper into the cash flow analysis of a prospective real estate deal. This is another tool to help an investor properly, effectively, and quickly analyze a property deal. For more information, please visit **www.RealEstateCashFlowAnalyzer.com**.

Real Estate Legal Plans – It's always recommended that you have an attorney review your contracts or other real estate legal documents. It can get quite costly to have one or more documents viewed by an attorney on a monthly basis. When you get to the point of having one or more documents looked at monthly by an attorney then you need to get on a legal plan to make it affordable. Each document review can cost you $250 to $500 minimum. Being on a monthly plan will cost a small fraction of that cost while giving you access to attorneys nationwide of all types of law expertise. Visit **www.RealEstateLegalPlans.com** for more information.

Commercial Appraisals – Do you want to put in an offer but you're not sure if your offer price is anywhere near what it will appraise out at? Consider getting a quick appraisal. Be sure to have all the details of your property deal together before you begin. You will need the property description and actual cash flow information to get an accurate appraisal. To get your "instant" commercial appraisal that will give you an estimated ballpark property value, visit **www.QuickCommercialAppraisal.com**.

Free Newsletter – Get Monica's monthly newsletter for free for 3 months. This is a newsletter that will offer you monthly information including which real estate markets are hot, which to avoid, new commercial investing information and investing strategies. To sign up for this newsletter, visit **www.MonicaMainNewsletter.com**.

To contact Monica Main directly, email **monica@monicamain.com**.

Multi-Unit Cash Flow System – Monica Main's latest real estate investing strategies are finally going to be revealed. As Monica progresses along and becomes a more savvy investor herself, she discovers new real estate investing strategies that are much more profitable than any of her other secrets that she's ever revealed. In the new multi-unit cash flow system, Monica will reveal the details of how to pick up small buildings including duplexes, triplexes, and "quads" among 5 – 12 unit apartment buildings for 100% cash for pennies on the dollar. The idea is to get a free and clear building with no debt service, fix it up, and lease it out while enjoying the maximum allowable cash flow. Small buildings generally have a 15% to 25% expense requirement against the GOI (Gross Operating Income). This is much less than larger buildings (which require 45% to 65% on average). For more information about her latest masterpiece, visit **www.MultiUnitMillionaire.com**

Mobile Home Park (MHP) Cash Flow – Discover the secrets of cashing in on MHPs with no cash and no credit. A new listing of MHP lenders allows for the new investor to get involved in a no-cash-no-credit MHP deal. These properties have the highest CAP rates (typically over 15%) which allows for the biggest possible monthly cash flow. Find out how you can start cashing in with the MHP Cash Flow System. For more information, go to **www.MHPCashFlow.com**.

Self-Storage Millionaire – Self-storage has quadrupled in popularity in the past 3 years because of the amount of people having to downsize from large homes into small apartment units or having to live with family and friends. Self-storage allows for the smallest amount of "tenant management" over all other types of commercial properties and yet the cash flow can be huge. Sell small spaces for big bucks! Learn how at **www.SelfStorageMillionaire.com**.

Protect Your Assets – Asset protection is *not* something you should take lightly. Most entrepreneurs, including real estate investors, assume that they don't have to consider using these techniques until they have money later on. The problem is this: if you don't set your LLCs and trusts up properly from the start, it is next to impossible to sort out the tightly-woven asset maze later on if you want to execute ultimate asset protection. Set up properly now, be protected forever. For more information, visit **www.BulletproofYourself.com**

Raising Private Money – Banks and conventional lenders are continuing to tighten up on their lending criteria. Even though commercial real estate offers the benefit of showing a solid cash flow to get banks to fork over the funds to purchase a property, personal and business credit is increasingly becoming more and more mandatory as time goes on. Seeking out private funds through angel investors and equity partnerships will soon be the mainstream way for a commercial real estate investor to purchase commercial properties. For more information, visit **www.MillionsInMinutes.com**.

Grant Writing Secrets Revealed – An underground grant-writing expert is revealing all the nitty-gritty details of how to get grant applications approved on both the federal and local levels of government. This is a former government employee who knows all the details about how to avoid getting the red-tape run-around, what to make sure you do on every application you submit, and exactly who you need to follow up with to get a status report on your application. For more information, visit **www.ThanksUncleSam.com**.

Rebuild Your Personal Credit – Personal credit is becoming increasingly important as time goes on. Having solid and pristine personal credit can make your real estate investing business much easier. It's fairly easy to bolster your personal credit with an easy step-by-step plan if you take the steps consistently. For more information, visit **www.RebuildPersonalCredit.com**.

Free Audio Seminar & Report for the Apartment Building Cash Flow System – Listen to Monica Main speak about why now is the best time to get involved in multifamily investing and how anyone can get started with no cash and no credit. For the audio seminar, please visit **www.ABCFSFreeAudio.com**. For her free report, visit **www.ApartmentBuildingFreeReport.com**.

Monica Main's 12-Month Apprenticeship Group – Become a member of Monica's *Exclusive Apprenticeship Group* which starts each summer. For information, visit **www.ApprenticeshipGroup.com**.

About the Author

Monica Main initially started investing in real estate in 1995 flipping single-family homes. She has been investing in passive income real estate for the past 10 years, focusing mostly on commercial property acquisitions including residential-commercial real estate.

Monica currently resides in Valencia, California with her young daughter.

For more information about Monica's products, services, seminars, and mentorship groups, please visit **www.MonicaMain.com**. You can email her directly at **monica@monicamain.com**.